Power Maths

Year 3 Practi Book 3B

Imagine you had £1,000.
What would you buy?
Draw it!

This book belongs to _____ .

My class is _____ .

Contents

This looks like a good challenge!

Unit 8 – Length

Unit 9 – Fractions (1)

It is time to do some practice!

3

How to use this book

Do you remember how to use this **Practice Book**?

Use the **Textbook** first to learn how to solve this type of problem.

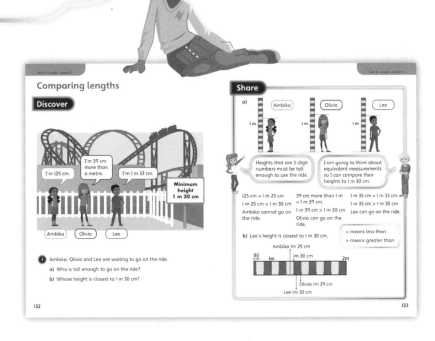

This shows you which **Textbook** page to use.

Have a go at questions by yourself using this **Practice Book**. Use what you have learnt.

Challenge questions make you think hard!

Questions with this light bulb make you think differently.

Reflect

Each lesson ends with a **Reflect** question so you can think about what you have learnt.

> Use **My power points** at the back of this book to keep track of what you have learnt.

Reflect

How would you solve each of these subtractions? What methods might you use?

a) 3 m 30 cm – 165 cm   b) 2 m – 1 m 30 cm

My journal

At the end of a unit your teacher will ask you to fill in **My journal**.

This will help you show how much you can do now that you have finished the unit.

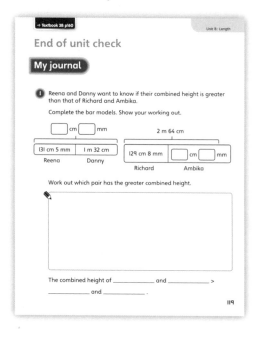

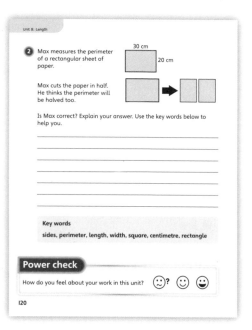

→ Textbook 3B p8

Comparing multiplication and division statements ①

① **a)** Who has the least number of biscuits?

Aki

Bella

5×10 ◯ 6×10

_____ has the least number of biscuits.

b) Who has the most cherries?

Zac

Amelia

☐ × ☐ ◯ ☐ × ☐

_____ has the most cherries.

② Which have the most spots in total, the butterflies or the ladybirds?

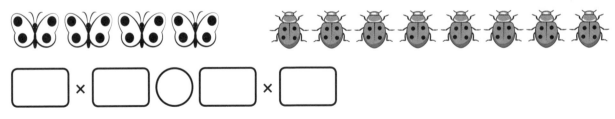

☐ × ☐ ◯ ☐ × ☐

The _____ have the most spots in total.

6

3 Jamie and Mo each have 20 cubes.

Jamie makes towers of 5 cubes.

Mo makes towers of 10 cubes.

Who makes the most towers?

$20 \div 5 \bigcirc 20 \div 10$

_____ makes the most towers.

4 Compare the following statements using <, > or =.

Try to complete them without working out the multiplications and divisions.

a) $8 \times 5 \bigcirc 10 \times 5$

b) $3 \times 3 \bigcirc 3 \times 1$

c) $4 \times 10 \bigcirc 8 \times 5$

d) $24 \div 4 \bigcirc 24 \div 8$

e) $7 \times 2 \bigcirc 9 \times 2$

f) $40 \div 8 \bigcirc 40 \div 5$

g) $24 \div 6 \bigcirc 24 \div 8$

5 Fill in numbers to make the sentences correct.

Try to complete them without working out the multiplications and divisions.

a) $5 \times 3 > \boxed{} \times 3$

b) $9 \times 4 = \boxed{} \times 9$

c) $12 \div \boxed{} > 12 \div 4$

d) $8 \times \boxed{} < \boxed{} \times 8$

6 Max has 2 identical bottles of milk.

He shares the first bottle equally between 5 glasses.

He shares the second bottle equally between 3 mugs.

Max wants to work out whether a glass or a mug has the most milk.

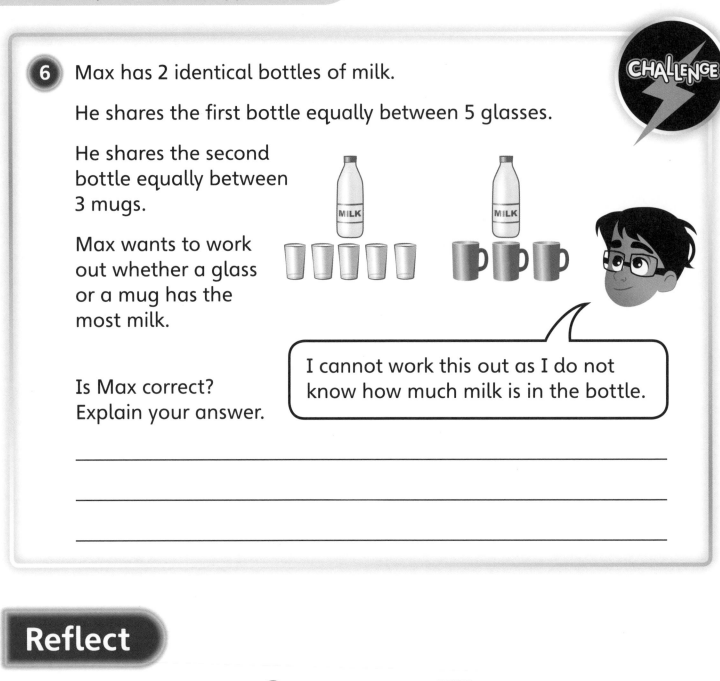

CHALLENGE

I cannot work this out as I do not know how much milk is in the bottle.

Is Max correct? Explain your answer.

_____

_____

_____

Reflect

What can you say about ● compared with ■ ?
Explain how you know.

● × 5 > ■ × 8   12 ÷ ● < 12 ÷ ■

Related multiplication calculations

1 How many pins are there?

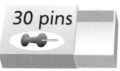

a) $2 \times 3 = \boxed{}$

There are $\boxed{}$ pins.

b) $2 \times 30 = \boxed{}$

There are $\boxed{}$ pins.

2 What is the score for each player?

Player 1

Player 2

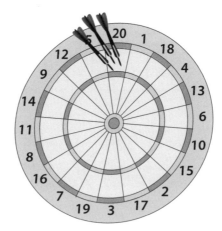

a) $\boxed{} \times \boxed{} = \boxed{}$

Player 1's score is $\boxed{}$.

b) $\boxed{} \times \boxed{} = \boxed{}$

Player 2's score is $\boxed{}$.

3 Jamie and Richard each have some money.

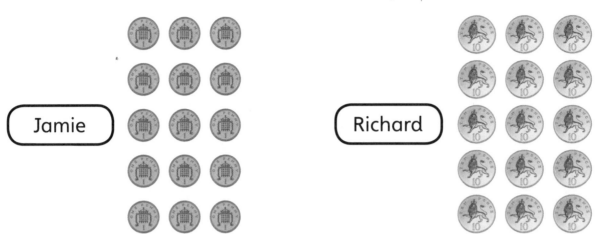

a) How much does Jamie have?

☐ × ☐ = ☐

Jamie has ☐ pence.

b) How much does Richard have?

☐ × ☐ = ☐

Richard has ☐ pence.

4 What multiplication calculations can you see?

a)

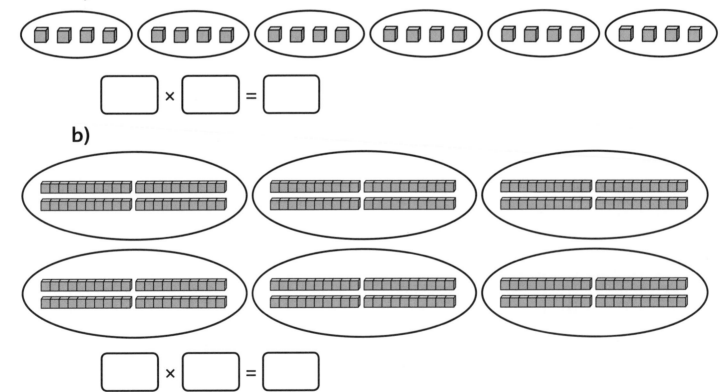

☐ × ☐ = ☐

b)

☐ × ☐ = ☐

5 Fill in numbers to make the multiplications correct.

a) $6 \times 4 = \boxed{}$

$6 \times 40 = \boxed{}$

b) $9 \times 5 = \boxed{}$

$9 \times 50 = \boxed{}$

c) $12 \times 30 = \boxed{}$

$8 \times 30 = \boxed{}$

$9 \times 30 = \boxed{}$

$30 \times 5 = \boxed{}$

d) $\boxed{} = 4 \times 20$

$\boxed{} = 20 \times 8$

$\boxed{} = 0 \times 20$

$\boxed{} = 11 \times 20$

6 Work out the answer to Holly's problem.

CHALLENGE

If I multiply my number by 5, I get 35. What do I get if I multiply my number by 50?

Explain how you got your answer.

_____

_____

Reflect

- Today I have learnt that if I know 4×8, I can work
- out _____ by
- _____
-

→ Textbook 3B p16

Related multiplication and division calculations

1 Share the cherries equally between the plates.

a)

$9 \div 3 = \boxed{}$

There are $\boxed{}$ cherries on each plate.

b)

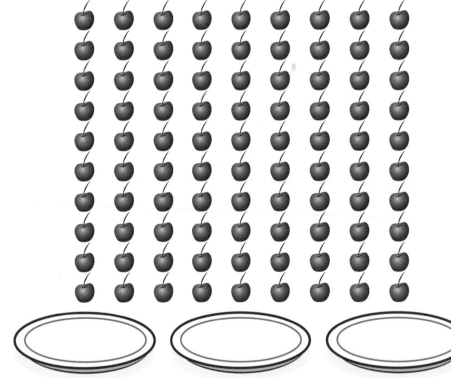

$90 \div 3 = \boxed{}$

There are $\boxed{}$ cherries on each plate.

2 Use the maths equipment to help you work out the calculations.

a)

$16 \div 2 = \boxed{}$

b)

$160 \div 2 = \boxed{}$

Did you use grouping or sharing to work out your answers?

3 What multiplication and division facts can you see?

a)

1	1	1	1	1	1
1	1	1	1	1	1
1	1	1	1	1	1
1	1	1	1	1	1

$\boxed{} \times \boxed{} = \boxed{}$

$\boxed{} \times \boxed{} = \boxed{}$

$\boxed{} \div \boxed{} = \boxed{}$

$\boxed{} \div \boxed{} = \boxed{}$

b)

10	10	10	10	10	10
10	10	10	10	10	10
10	10	10	10	10	10
10	10	10	10	10	10

$\boxed{} \times \boxed{} = \boxed{}$

$\boxed{} \times \boxed{} = \boxed{}$

$\boxed{} \div \boxed{} = \boxed{}$

$\boxed{} \div \boxed{} = \boxed{}$

4 Fill in numbers to make the sentences correct.

a) $24 \div 3 = \boxed{}$

$240 \div 3 = \boxed{}$

$36 \div 4 = \boxed{}$

$360 \div 4 = \boxed{}$

b) $280 \div 4 = \boxed{}$

$350 \div 5 = \boxed{}$

$700 \div 10 = \boxed{}$

$270 \div 3 = \boxed{}$

c) $8 \times \boxed{} = 160$

$320 \div \boxed{} = 40$

$\boxed{} \times 30 = 330$

$\boxed{} \div 4 = 50$

5 Jess spends 240 pence in a shop.

What could she have bought?

How many different answers can you find?

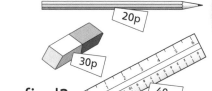

_____

_____

Reflect

I know $8 \times 3 = 24$, so I also know _____

_____

How many related multiplications and divisions do you know?

How did you work them out?

_____

_____

Comparing multiplication and division statements ❷

1   Are there more mints in total in the tubes or in the bags?

$6 \times 20 \bigcirc 7 \times 20$

There are more mints in total in the _____ .

2   Complete the sentences to make the statements correct.

a)

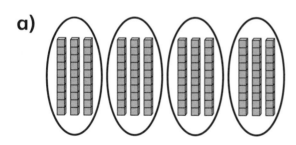 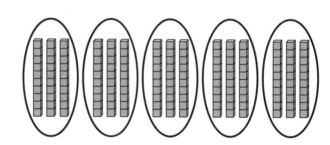

$4 \times 30 \bigcirc 5 \times 30$

b)

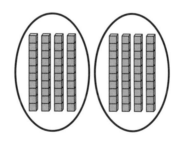

3 **a)** 240 sweets are shared between 3 boxes.

240 sweets are shared between 4 bags.

Does a box or a bag contain more sweets?

240 ÷ ☐ ◯ 240 ÷ ☐

A _____ contains more sweets.

How do you know without working out any calculation?

_____

_____

_____

b) 90 marbles are shared among 3 children.

120 marbles are shared among 4 adults.

How many marbles do they each receive?

Each child receives ☐ marbles. Each adult receives ☐
marbles.

What do you notice? Why do you think this is?

_____

_____

_____

4 Compare the following statements using <, > or =.

a) 3 × 50 ◯ 7 × 50   **d)** 9 × 50 ◯ 8 × 50

b) 4 × 80 ◯ 4 × 20   **e)** 180 ÷ 2 ◯ 180 ÷ 9

c) 50 × 4 ◯ 3 × 50   **f)** 80 ÷ 2 ◯ 60 ÷ 2

5 Look at these calculations.

CHALLENGE

 × 60 < × 60

350 ÷ > 350 ÷

120 ÷ > 80 ÷

Match the correct number to the correct symbol.

4	5	6	7	8

Reflect

Describe the numbers that can go into the boxes.

☐ × 40 > 3 × 40   120 ÷ 4 < 120 ÷ ☐

Explain how you know.

_____

_____

_____

→ Textbook 3B p24

Multiplying a 2-digit number by a 1-digit number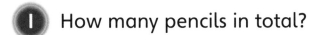

1 How many pencils in total?

2 × 3 ones = ☐ ones

2 × 3 = ☐

☐ × ☐ tens = ☐ tens

☐ × ☐ = ☐

☐ + ☐ = ☐

So, 2 × 43 = ☐

There are ☐ pencils in total.

T	O
🔟🔟 🔟🔟	▯▯▯
🔟🔟 🔟🔟	▯▯▯

2 How many in total?

☐ × ☐ 1s = ☐ 1s

☐ × ☐ = ☐

☐ × ☐ 10s = ☐ 10s

☐ × ☐ = ☐

☐ + ☐ = ☐

So, ☐ × ☐ = ☐

There are ☐ in total.

T	O
🔟🔟	▯▯
🔟🔟	▯▯
🔟🔟	▯▯
🔟🔟	▯▯

3 Use the place value grids to work out the following multiplications.

a) 32 × 3

☐ × ☐ 1s = ☐ 1s

☐ × ☐ = ☐

☐ × ☐ 10s = ☐ 10s

☐ × ☐ = ☐

☐ + ☐ = ☐   So, 32 × 3 = ☐

T	O
10 10 10	1 1
10 10 10	1 1
10 10 10	1 1

b) 22 × 4

☐ × ☐ 1s = ☐ 1s

☐ × ☐ = ☐

☐ × ☐ 10s = ☐ 10s

☐ × ☐ = ☐

☐ + ☐ = ☐   So, 22 × 4 = ☐

T	O
10 10	1 1
10 10	1 1
10 10	1 1
10 10	1 1

4 Find the solution to these calculations.

a) 14 × 2 = ☐   **b)** 3 × 33 = ☐

5 Olivia uses a different method to work out answers.

a) Use Olivia's method to work out 2 × 23.

I multiplied the 10s and then the 1s and then added them together.

b) Work these out mentally.

24 × 2 = ☐

32 × 3 = ☐

2 × 43 = ☐

My method helps me work out the answers in my head.

Reflect

In order to work out 3 × 13, first I would _____

_____

Then I would _____

_____

Finally I would _____

_____

Multiplying a 2-digit number by a 1-digit number ❷

1 Work out the answer to each of these multiplications.

a) 3 × 24

$3 \times 4 = \boxed{}$

$3 \times 20 = \boxed{}$

$\boxed{} + \boxed{} = \boxed{}$

$3 \times 24 = \boxed{}$

T	O

b) 5 × 13

$\boxed{} \times \boxed{} = \boxed{}$

$\boxed{} \times \boxed{} = \boxed{}$

$\boxed{} + \boxed{} = \boxed{}$

$5 \times 13 = \boxed{}$

T	O

c) 2 × 28

$\boxed{} \times \boxed{} = \boxed{}$

$\boxed{} \times \boxed{} = \boxed{}$

$\boxed{} + \boxed{} = \boxed{}$

$2 \times 28 = \boxed{}$

T	O

2 Use the place value grids to work out the following multiplications.

a) 35 × 3

T	O
⑩ ⑩ ⑩	① ① ① ① ①
⑩ ⑩ ⑩	① ① ① ① ①
⑩ ⑩ ⑩	① ① ① ① ①

☐ × ☐ = ☐

☐ × ☐ = ☐

☐ + ☐ = ☐

35 × 3 = ☐

b) 4 × 25

T	O
⑩ ⑩	① ① ① ① ①
⑩ ⑩	① ① ① ① ①
⑩ ⑩	① ① ① ① ①
⑩ ⑩	① ① ① ① ①

☐ × ☐ = ☐

☐ × ☐ = ☐

☐ + ☐ = ☐

4 × 25 = ☐

3 Work out the following calculations.

a) 3 × 26 = ☐

b) 6 × 14 = ☐

4 How much paint is there in total in 33 tins?

5 litres

There are ☐ litres of paint in total.

22

5 Complete the multiplications using the working out calculations.

a)
$3 \times 7 = 21$
$3 \times 10 = 30$

$3 \times \boxed{} = 51$

b)
$18 + 80 = 98$

$2 \times \boxed{} = 98$

6 Match the multiplication to the answer.

Can you match them without working out the answers?

56×3

26×8

37×5

208

185

168

Use the space below to show your method for each one.

Reflect

What is the same and what is different about these calculations?

$36 \times 4 = \boxed{}$

$72 \times 2 = \boxed{}$

→ Textbook 3B p32

Multiplying a 2-digit number by a 1-digit number ❸

① Work out the answer to each of these multiplications.

a) 25 × 3

T	O

```
  T  O
  2  5
×    3
_____

        5 × 3
+       20 × 3
_____
```

b) 17 × 4

T	O

```
  T  O
  1  7
×    4
_____

        7 × 4
+       10 × 4
_____
```

② Work out the following multiplications.

a) 16 × 3

```
  T  O
  1  6
×    3
_____


+ _____
_____
```

b) 48 × 2

```
  T  O
  4  8
×    2
_____


+ _____
_____
```

24

3 Work out the multiplications using a column method.

a) $14 \times 5 = \boxed{}$

b) $4 \times 19 = \boxed{}$

4 Ambika used these digits to make a multiplication. $\boxed{1} \boxed{2} \boxed{4}$

Work out where the digits go in each multiplication.

a)
```
    T  O
  _____
×
  _____
       8
+ 4  0
  _____
```

b)
```
    T  O
  _____
×
  _____
       4
+
    8  4
  _____
```

5 Jamie is working out 26×1.

Could Jamie have worked it out an easier way? Explain how.

```
    T  O
  _____
    2  6
×      1
  _____
       6
+ 2  0
  _____
    2  6
  _____
```

_____

_____

_____

6 Work out the following multiplications.

a) 35 × 3

```
    T  O
    3  5
×      3
────────

+  ─────
   ─────
```

b) 18 × 6

```
    T  O
    1  8
×      6
────────

+  ─────
   ─────
```

7 Work out the answer to the following multiplication.

CHALLENGE

I might try and work out what each symbol is worth first.

Explain your reasoning.

_____

_____

_____

Reflect

Explain how to set out and complete 23 × 5 using a column method.

_____

_____

_____

Dividing a 2-digit number by a 1-digit number ❶

1 Share 28 apples equally between 2 baskets.

2 tens ÷ 2 = ☐ ten

20 ÷ 2 = ☐

8 ones ÷ 2 = ☐ ones

8 ÷ 2 = ☐

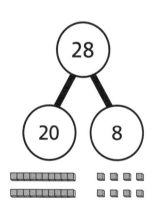

☐ + ☐ = ☐

28 ÷ 2 = ☐

Each basket has ☐ apples.

2 **a)** Work out $69 \div 3$.

6 tens $\div 3 = \boxed{}$ tens

$60 \div 3 = \boxed{}$

$\boxed{}$ ones $\div \boxed{} = \boxed{}$ ones

$\boxed{} \div \boxed{} = \boxed{}$

$\boxed{} + \boxed{} = \boxed{}$ So, $69 \div 3 = \boxed{}$

b) Work out $88 \div 4$.

$\boxed{}$ tens $\div \boxed{} = \boxed{}$ tens

$\boxed{} \div \boxed{} = \boxed{}$

$\boxed{}$ ones $\div \boxed{} = \boxed{}$ ones

$\boxed{} \div \boxed{} = \boxed{}$

$\boxed{} + \boxed{} = \boxed{}$ So, $88 \div 4 = \boxed{}$

3 Divide 85 by 5 by dividing the tens first and then the ones.

Show your method.

4 Work out the division calculations that Luis is trying to solve.

a) ⬜ ÷ 3 = 32

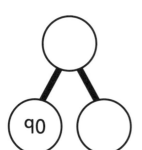

90 ÷ 3 = 30   ⬜ ÷ 3 = 2

b) ⬜ ÷ 2 = ⬜

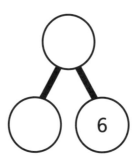

⬜ ÷ 2 = 40   6 ÷ 2 = 3

5 Use 4 different digits to complete the calculation below.

CHALLENGE

| 1 | 2 | 3 | 6 | 9 |

⬜⬜ ÷ 3 = ⬜⬜

How many different answers can you find?

_____

_____

Reflect

- To work out 84 ÷ 4, first I would _____

- Then I would _____

- Finally, I would _____

→ Textbook 3B p40

Dividing a 2-digit number by a 1-digit number ❷

 a) Work out 45 ÷ 3.

30 ÷ 3 = ☐

15 ÷ 3 = ☐

☐ + ☐ = ☐

45 ÷ 3 = ☐

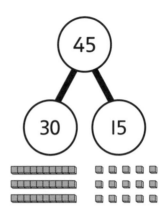

b) Work out 34 ÷ 2.

20 ÷ 2 = ☐

14 ÷ 2 = ☐

☐ + ☐ = ☐

34 ÷ 2 = ☐

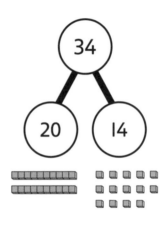

c) Work out 65 ÷ 5.

☐ ÷ 5 = ☐

☐ ÷ 5 = ☐

☐ + ☐ = ☐

65 ÷ 5 = ☐

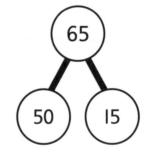

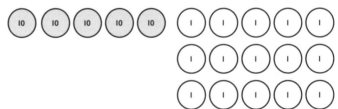

2 Complete the calculations to help Emma and Aki work out $78 \div 3$.

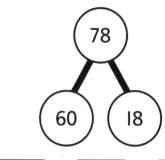

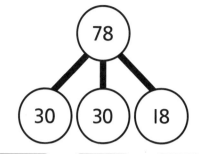

$\boxed{} \div \boxed{} = \boxed{}$

$\boxed{} \div \boxed{} = \boxed{}$

$\boxed{} + \boxed{} = \boxed{}$

$78 \div 3 = \boxed{}$

$\boxed{} \div \boxed{} = \boxed{}$

$\boxed{} \div \boxed{} = \boxed{}$

$\boxed{} \div \boxed{} = \boxed{}$

$\boxed{} + \boxed{} + \boxed{} = \boxed{}$

$78 \div 3 = \boxed{}$

3 Work out the following divisions.

a) $72 \div 2 = \boxed{}$

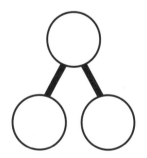

b) $72 \div 3 = \boxed{}$

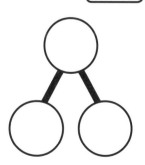

c) $85 \div 5 = \boxed{}$

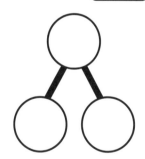

d) $57 \div 3 = \boxed{}$

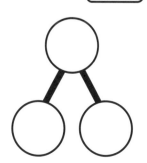

31

4 Mr Lopez has a tray of 84 cubes.

Each child needs 3 cubes.

There are 27 children in the class.

Are there enough cubes for each child to have 3?

5 Work out the missing digits.

CHALLENGE

a) $\boxed{}2 \div 4 = 1\boxed{}$ b) $9\boxed{} \div 5 = 1\boxed{}$ c) $\boxed{}4 \div 3 = \boxed{}8$

Reflect

Which of the following part-whole models does not help you work out 92 ÷ 4?

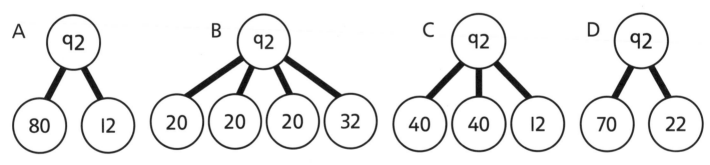

A 92 — 80, 12

B 92 — 20, 20, 20, 32

C 92 — 40, 40, 12

D 92 — 70, 22

Explain why it does not help.

_____

_____

Dividing a 2-digit number by a 1-digit number ③

1 There are 45 tins of peas.

The tins are stacked on 2 shelves.

A shopkeeper wants to put the same number of tins on each shelf.

a) How many tins can go on each shelf?

$40 ÷ 2 = \boxed{}$

$5 ÷ 2 = \boxed{}$ remainder $\boxed{}$

$45 ÷ 2 = \boxed{}$ remainder $\boxed{}$

$\boxed{}$ tins can go on each shelf.

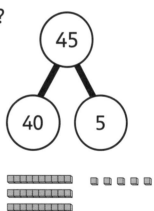

b) How many tins cannot be put on the shelf?

The remainder is $\boxed{}$ so $\boxed{}$ tin cannot be put on the shelf.

2 **a)** Complete the sentence.

I know there will be a remainder when I divide 53 by 4 because _____

_____

_____

b) Work out 53 ÷ 4.

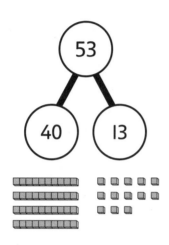

We can use the letter r to mean remainder.

☐ ÷ ☐ = ☐

☐ ÷ ☐ = ☐ r ☐

53 ÷ 4 = ☐ r ☐

3 Work out the following divisions.

a) 83 ÷ 4 = ☐ r ☐

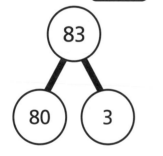

c) 83 ÷ 3 = ☐ r ☐

83

b) 83 ÷ 5 = ☐ r ☐

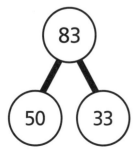

d) 83 ÷ 8 = ☐ r ☐

83

34

4 ⬚ ÷ 5 = 15 r 2

Find the missing number.

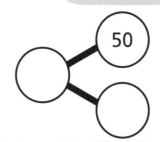

5

My number is between 50 and 60.

When I divide my number by 3 it has a remainder of 2.

When I divide my number by 4 it has a remainder of 1.

I am thinking of a number.

CHALLENGE

What could Ambika's number be?

_____

_____

Reflect

Pick one of the following divisions.

67 ÷ 2   67 ÷ 3   67 ÷ 4   67 ÷ 5

How do you know it will have a remainder?

  _____

_____

Work out the division.

  _____

→ **Textbook 3B p48**

How many ways?

1 Bella needs some glasses and shoes.

There are 3 pairs of glasses and 3 pairs of shoes she can choose from.

A  B  C

1  2  3

a) List all the possible ways Bella can choose the glasses and shoes.
(You may not need to use the whole of the tables.)

Glasses	Shoes

Glasses	Shoes

b) How many different ways are there?

☐ × ☐ = ☐

There are ☐ ways.

Did you find all the ways?
If you found more or less
ways, check your answers.

36

2 Richard has 5 symbol cards and 2 letter cards.

X

Y

Richard picks a symbol card and a letter card.

a) How many different ways could he do this?

$\boxed{} \times \boxed{} = \boxed{}$

There are $\boxed{}$ ways.

b) Show all the ways in the table below.

Symbol	Letter

Symbol	Letter

Symbol	Letter

c) Richard now has 6 symbol cards and 4 letter cards.

He picks a symbol card and a letter card.

How many different possible ways are there?

There are $\boxed{}$ ways.

③ Zac picks a piece of fruit and a snack.

How many different possible ways are there?

There are ⬚ ways.

Fruit

Snacks

④ Choose 3 different colouring pencils.

CHALLENGE

A flag is made up of 2 different colours and is divided in half vertically.

How many different flags can you make, using all 3 of your colouring pencils?

I can make ⬚ flags.

Explain your answer.

_____

_____

Reflect

To work out the number of ways in question 3 I would _____

_____

Problem solving – mixed problems

1 There are 15 cakes on a tray.

 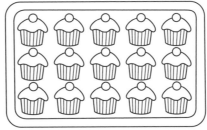 

How many cakes are there on 3 trays?

?

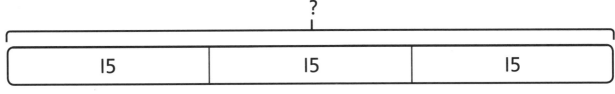

| 15 | 15 | 15 |

There are ☐ cakes in total.

2 There are 64 items of clothing in this chest of drawers.

There is the same number of items in each drawer.

How many items of clothing are in each drawer?

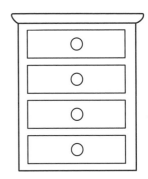

64

There are ☐ items of clothing in each drawer.

3 a) A jar contains 8 spoonfuls of honey.

Each spoonful holds 12 ml of honey.

How much honey is in the jar?

There are [ ] ml of honey in the jar.

b) The honey is poured equally onto 3 bowls of porridge.

How much honey is in each bowl?

There are [ ] ml of honey in each bowl.

4 A tower is 3 times as tall as a house.

A house is 34 metres tall.

How tall is the tower?

The tower is [ ] metres tall.

40

5 Work out the missing number.

$26 \times 3 = \boxed{} \times 2$

Use the bar model to help you.

26	26	26

6 5 books costs £85.

£85

How much do 2 of these books cost?

2 books cost £ [   ].

Reflect

Max used this bar model to help him solve a problem.

What could the problem have been?

72

18	18	18	18

Problem solving – mixed problems ❷

1 Ice creams are sold in boxes of 3 or boxes of 5.

Kate buys the following ice creams.

3 ice creams   3 ice creams   3 ice creams   3 ice creams

5 ice creams   5 ice creams   5 ice creams   5 ice creams   5 ice creams   5 ice creams

How many ice creams does she buy in total?

$\boxed{} \times 3 = \boxed{}$

$\boxed{} \times 5 = \boxed{}$

$\boxed{} + \boxed{} = \boxed{}$

Kate buys $\boxed{}$ ice creams in total.

2 A basket contains 5 apples and 8 pears.

There are 7 baskets.

How many more pears than apples are there?

There are $\boxed{}$ more pears than apples.

3 A bag of balloons contains 5 red and 3 blue balloons.

a) How many balloons in 6 bags?

There are ⬜ balloons in 6 bags.

b) Reena needs 80 balloons for a birthday party.

How many packs does she need to buy?

Reena needs to buy ⬜ packs.

4 Rulers are sold in boxes of 5.

Mrs Dean has 3 boxes of rulers.
Mr Jones has 4 boxes of rulers.

Work out how many rulers they
have altogether.

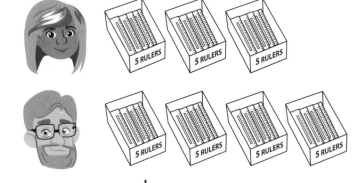

5	5	5

Mrs Dean

5	5	5	5

Mr Jones

$3 \times 5 + 4 \times 5 = \boxed{} \times 5$

They have ⬜ rulers altogther.

5 Work out the missing numbers.

a) $4 \times 3 + 5 \times 3 = \boxed{} \times 3$

b) $8 \times 5 + \boxed{} \times 5 = 12 \times 5$

c) $3 \times 8 + 8 = \boxed{} \times 8$

d) $7 \times 4 - 2 \times 4 = \boxed{} \times 4$

e) $5 \times 2 + 8 = \boxed{} \times 2$

Use a bar model to help you.

6 2 eggs and a slice of toast cost 60 pence.

2 eggs and 3 slices of toast cost 96 pence.

Work out the cost of an egg.

CHALLENGE

The cost of an egg is $\boxed{}$ pence.

Reflect

A box contains 5 yellow counters and 3 blue counters.

There are 6 boxes of these counters.

Explain two ways you can work out the total number of counters.

Problem solving – mixed problems ③

1 **a)** The beads below are shared between 3 people.

How many beads does each person receive?

Each person receives ☐ beads.

b) The same beads are shared between 4 people.

How many beads does each person receive?

Each person receives ☐ beads.

2 Work out the missing value below.

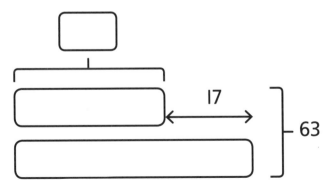

17

63

3 There are 35 children at a play.

3 times as many adults are at the play.

How many people in total are at the play?

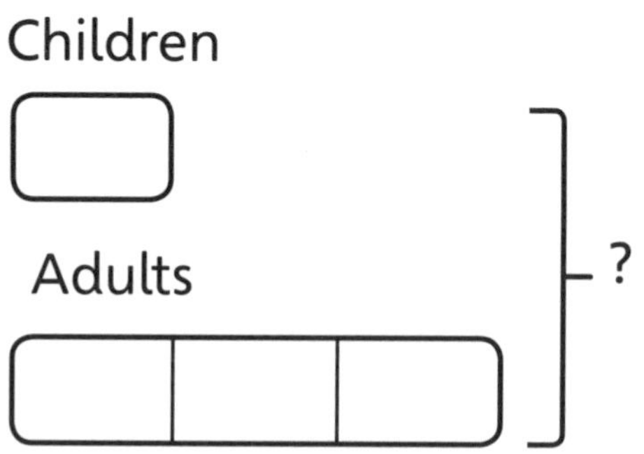

Children

Adults

?

There are ⬚ people in total at the play.

4 Here are some balance scales.

5 kg 5 kg
5 kg 5 kg
5 kg 5 kg 500 g

Work out the weight of the baby giraffe.

The baby giraffe weighs ⬚ kg.

5 Potatoes are sold in 2 kg and 5 kg sacks.

Max buys 50 kg of potatoes in total.

He buys 10 of the 2 kg sacks.

How many 5 kg sacks does he buy?

2 kg   **5 kg**

Max buys [ ] 5 kg sacks.

6 Danny and Isla are each thinking of a number.

Work out their numbers.

CHALLENGE

My number is 74 more than yours.

Isla

Danny's number is [ ] .

Danny

Isla's number is [ ] .

Our numbers add together to make 150.

Reflect

Which problem did you find the easiest to solve?

Which problem did you find most challenging? Why?

→ Textbook 3B p64

End of unit check

My journal

1 Imagine you are the teacher.

Explain to your class how to work out the following calculations.

a) 8 × 15

b) 87 ÷ 3

I would use diagrams and equipment to help me, not just work out the calculation.

2 Look at these multiplications.

0 × 3 = 0	20 × 3 = 60
1 × 3 = 3	21 × 3 = 63
2 × 3 = 6	22 × 3 = 66
3 × 3 = 9	23 × 3 = 69
4 × 3 = 12	24 × 3 = 72
5 × 3 = 15	25 × 3 = 75
6 × 3 = 18	26 × 3 = 78
7 × 3 = 21	27 × 3 = 81
8 × 3 = 24	28 × 3 = 84
9 × 3 = 27	29 × 3 = 87
10 × 3 = 30	30 × 3 = 90

Look at the the last digits of the answers in the second column.

a) Predict what the last digits of these multiplications will be.

36 × 3	72 × 3	155 × 3	765 × 3	999 × 3
☐	☐	☐	☐	☐

b) What about these?

34 × 2	49 × 2	55 × 5	72 × 8	139 × 4
☐	☐	☐	☐	☐

Power check

How do you feel about your work in this unit?

Power puzzle

Use the digit cards to make each calculation correct.

1 a) ☐☐ × ☐ = ☐☐☐

| 0 | 0 | 1 | 3 | 6 | 8 |

b) ☐ × ☐ + ☐ × ☐ = ☐☐ × ☐

| 1 | 4 | 4 | 4 | 5 | 6 | 9 |

c)

```
    H   T   O
       ☐   ☐
  ×        ☐
       _____
           ☐
  + ☐   ☐   ☐
   _____
    ☐   ☐   ☐
```

| 0 | 1 | 1 | 2 | 2 |
| 2 | 3 | 4 | 8 | 8 |

Create your own questions for your partner to try!

50

Pounds and pence

1 **a)** How much money is there?

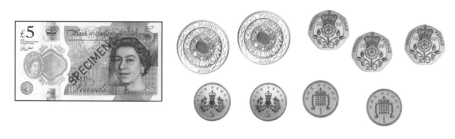

There is ☐ pounds and ☐ pence.

b)

There is £ ☐ and ☐ p.

c)

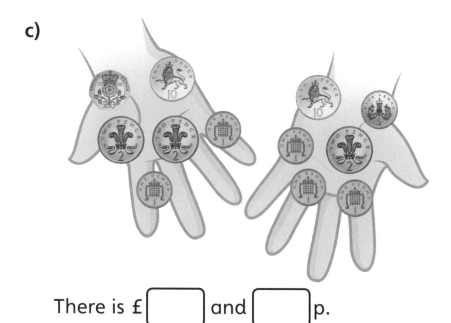

There is £ ☐ and ☐ p.

2 Circle the money you need to make these amounts.

a) £4 and 20p

b) £7 and 59p

3 Max has these coins:

He chooses 5 of his coins.

a) Show two ways he can make £2 and 50p with 5 coins.

b) What is the greatest amount he can make with 5 coins?

The greatest amount he can make is £ ☐ and ☐ p.

4 What is the fewest number of coins you need to make £2 and 48p?

Draw the coins.

5 Kate has £14 and 35p. Zac has the following money:

CHALLENGE

Richard has more money than Kate, but less than Zac.

Richard has 3 notes and 8 coins.

What notes and coins could Richard have?

Reflect

Reena says that she has £3 and 20p.
What mistake could Reena have made?

Converting pounds and pence

1 Tick the sets of coins that make £1.

a)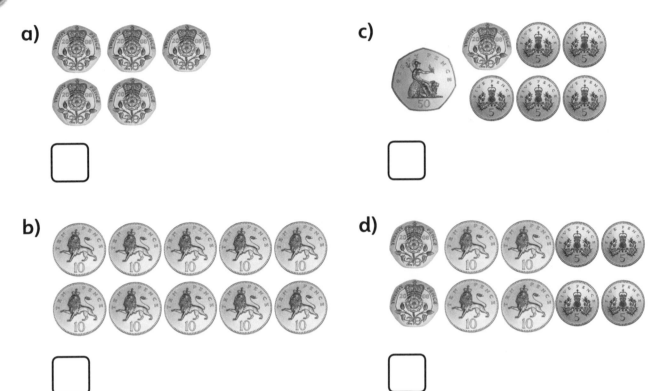

c)

b)

d)

2 How much money was in the money box?

There was ☐ p in the money box.

This is the same as £ ☐ and ☐ p.

3 Work out how much money each child has.

a)

Ambika has £ ☐ and ☐ p.

b)

Max has £ ☐ and ☐ p.

4 Complete the part-whole models.

a)

268p

£2 ☐

c)

450p

☐ ☐

b)

394p

£☐ ☐ p

d)

☐ p

£7 24p

5 Complete the following sentences.

a) 350p = £3 and ⬚ p

e) ⬚ p = £3 and 8p

b) 429p = £⬚ and ⬚ p

f) 4⬚ p = £⬚ and 48p

c) 504p = £⬚ and ⬚ p

g) 1,870p = £⬚ and ⬚ p

d) ⬚ p = £1 and 85p

6 Complete the table to show how many of each coin make £3.

CHALLENGE

Coin	Number of coins needed to make £3
£1	3
50p	
20p	
10p	
5p	
2p	
1p	300

Reflect

Explain why £2 and 72p is equal to 272 pence.

Adding money

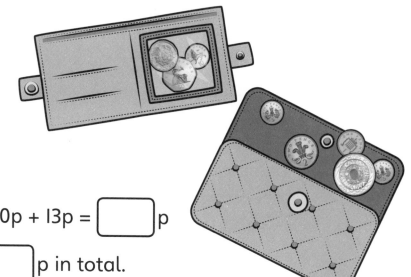

1 How much money in total?

a)

£1 + £2 = £ [ ] and 60p + 13p = [ ]p

There is £ [ ] and [ ]p in total.

b)

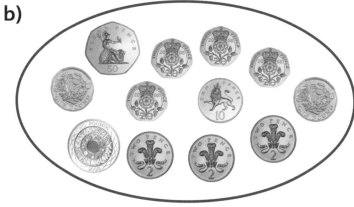 

£ [ ] + £ [ ] = £ [ ]

[ ]p + [ ]p = [ ]p

There is £ [ ] and [ ]p in total.

2 What is the total cost?

£1 + £2 = £ [ ]

35p + 42p = [ ]p

The total cost is £ [ ] and [ ]p.

3 Work out how much each person pays.

Tea   £1 and 40p
Coffee   £1 and 60p
Sandwich   £2 and 55p
Cheese on Toast £1 and 78p

a)

> Please can I have a sandwich and a cup of tea?

The total cost is £ ☐ and ☐ p.

b)

> May I have a cup of coffee and a sandwich, please?

The total cost is £ ☐ and ☐ p.

> Try to work some of these out in your head. Check your answers using a written method.

4 Work out these additions.

a) £2 and 10p + £3 and 45p = £ ☐ and ☐ p

b) £1 and 42p + £5 and 39p = £ ☐ and ☐ p

c) £4 and 45p + £2 and 70p = £ ☐ and ☐ p

d) £6 and 47p + 75p = £ ☐ and ☐ p

e) £14 + 286p = £ ☐ and ☐ p

5 Here are some items for sale in a sports shop.

CHALLENGE

£2 and 56p

£6 and 40p

£2 and 4p

£2 and 69p

a) Which two items add together to make the greatest cost?

_____

b) What is this cost?

_____

c) Which two items add to make £4 and 60p?

_____

d) Which two items add to 525p?

_____

Reflect

Add together £2 and 36p and £2 and 87p. Explain your method.

_____

_____

_____

Subtracting amounts of money

1 Mia has the following coins:

She spends £5 and 47p.

How much money does she have left?

Mia has £ ⬚ and ⬚ p left.

2 Max has the following money:

He buys a T-shirt costing £7 and 90p.

How much money does he have left?

Max has £ ⬚ and ⬚ p left.

I am going to exchange one of the coins for different coins to help me. Then I can cross them out.

3 Here are some items on sale in a bicycle shop.

a) How much more does the helmet cost than the pump?

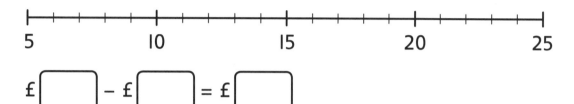

£⬚ – £⬚ = £⬚

The helmet costs £⬚ more than the pump.

b) How much less than the bike does the helmet cost?

✏️

£⬚ – £⬚ = £⬚

The helmet costs £⬚ less than the bike.

4 Work out the difference between:

£6 and 30p and £5 and 85p

The difference is _____ .

5 Work out:

a) £1 and 85p – £1 and 42p

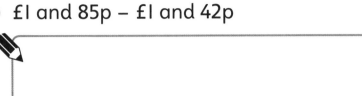

b) £4 and 12p – £3 and 80p

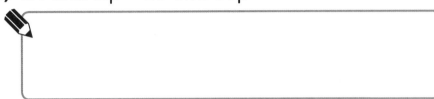

c) £7 – 84p

You might want to make the amounts by drawing the coins and crossing out, or you could use a number line.

d) £3 and 92p – £2 and 97p

Reflect

Show the method you would use to work out £2 and 40p – £1 and 55p.

Problem solving – money

1 Richard buys a pair of boots and some socks.

a) What is the total cost?

The total cost is £ ☐ .

b) How much change does Richard get from a £20 note?

Richard gets £ ☐ change.

2 Marie buys a sandwich for £2 and 70p.

She pays with this note.

How much change does Marie get?

Marie gets £ ☐ and ☐ p change.

3 The prices of some items are shown below.

£2 and 60p

£1 and 95p

£3 and 80p

Draw lines to match the word problem to its number sentence.

The total cost of 3 packs of pencils.

£2 and 60p + £1 and 95p

The total cost of the pencils and pack of cards.

£2 and 60p – £1 and 95p

The cost of 1 ball of string.

£2 and 60p multiplied by 3

The difference between the cost of the pencils and the pack of cards.

Half of £3 and 80p

Use this space for your working.

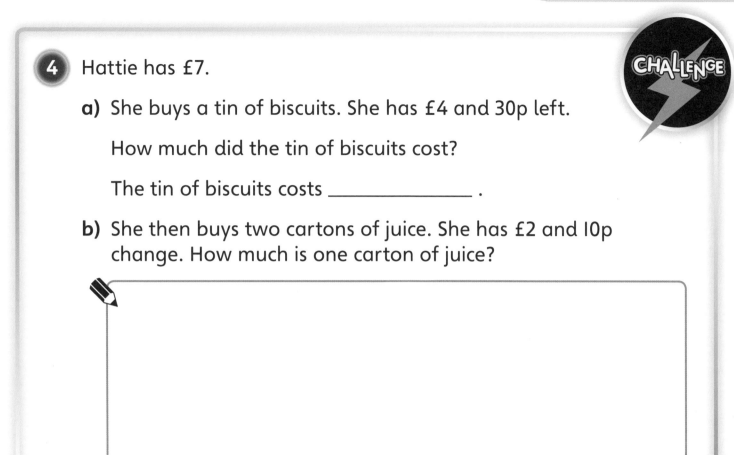

4 Hattie has £7.

a) She buys a tin of biscuits. She has £4 and 30p left.

How much did the tin of biscuits cost?

The tin of biscuits costs _____ .

b) She then buys two cartons of juice. She has £2 and 10p change. How much is one carton of juice?

One carton of juice costs _____ .

Reflect

Make up your own addition or subtraction problem for a partner to solve. Write your word problem below.

£1 and 20p   £2 and 75p   £1 and 79p

→ **Textbook 3B p88**

End of unit check

My journal

Jamie

1 Make up your own story that the images might describe.

What problem could go with your story?

_____

_____

_____

_____

_____

_____

_____

_____

Power check

How do you feel about your work in this unit?

Power puzzle

Max is buying ingredients to bake a cake.

400 g butter	£1 and 75
1 egg	20p
100 g sugar	35p
100 g flour	26p
100 g cocoa	£1 and 80
1 pack of sprinkles	87p

He uses the following recipe to make a cake:

400 g butter

2 eggs

400 g sugar

400 g flour

50 g cocoa

One pack of sprinkles

What strategy did you use to add up all the amounts? Is there a different way you could have found the answer?

He just buys the amount of each ingredient he needs.

How much change from £10 would Max get?

Max would get £ [ ] and [ ] p change.

67

→ Textbook 3B p92

Pictograms

1 Luis made a pictogram about children's favourite fruit.

How many children said their favourite fruit was an orange?

Orange has 3 symbols.

Each 😃 symbol represents ⬜ children.

3 × ⬜ = ⬜

⬜ children said their favourite fruit was an orange.

Key: Each 😃 represents 2 children.	

Fruit	Number of children
apple	😃 😃 😃 😃
banana	😃 😃 😃 😃
pear	😃 😃 😃
orange	😃 😃 😃

2 Andy asked his friends about their favourite snack.

Key: Each 🍪 represents 10 children.

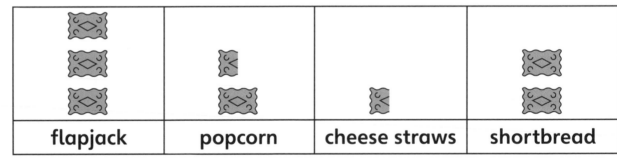

flapjack	popcorn	cheese straws	shortbread

Complete the sentences.

a) 🍪 represents _____ .

⬜ children said popcorn was their favourite snack.

b) ⬜ children said cheese straws were their favourite snack.

c) More children like _____ or _____ than like popcorn.

68

3 Amelia asked all of Key Stage 2 about their favourite drink.

Complete the pictogram.

Key: Each ⬜ represents 10 children.

Drink	Number of children
water	50
orange juice	35
apple juice	20
blackcurrant squash	25

Drink	Number of children
water	⬜⬜⬜⬜⬜
orange juice	
apple juice	
blackcurrant squash	

4 Jamilla asked some children about their favourite treat foods.

Complete the table and the pictogram.

Key: Each 🧁 represents ⬜ children.

Treat	Number of children
cake	
chocolate bar	10
chewy sweets	
fruit	
yoghurt	20

Treat	Number of children
cake	🧁🧁🧁🧁
chocolate bar	🧁🧁
chewy sweets	🧁🧁🧁
fruit	🧁
yoghurt	

5 Isla made two pictograms to show the amount of sugar in some drinks made by two different companies.

Fizz Bizz

Drink	Sugar content
cola	▦
orangeade	▦

Key:
Each ▦ represents 10 g sugar.

Posh Squash

Drink	Sugar content
summer fruits	▦ ▦ ▦ ▦
orangeade	▦ ▦ ▦

Key:
Each ▦ represents 2 g sugar.

a) Which company's orangeade contains least sugar?

_____ company's orangeade contains the least sugar.

b) Explain how Isla could make her charts more helpful.

_____

_____

Reflect

Create a section of a pictogram which shows that 10 people have chosen Hide and Seek as their favourite game.

Make two versions, each with a different key.

70

Pictograms ❷

1 Some people were asked their favourite holiday destination. The pictogram shows the results.

Destination	Number of people
Spain	🧳 🧳
Portugal	🧳 🧳 🧳
France	🧳 🧳
Greece	🧳 🧳 🧳

Key: Each 🧳 = 10 people.

a) How many more people chose Greece than France?

There are ⬚ symbols for Greece and ⬚ for France.

⬚ – ⬚ = ⬚

1 symbol represents ⬚ .

⬚ × ⬚ = ⬚

⬚ more people said Greece was their favourite destination.

b) How many people chose Greece or Portugal?

⬚ people chose Greece or Portugal.

Show your working out in the box below.

2 How many people were asked altogether?

There are ☐ symbols in the pictogram altogether.

Each symbol represents ☐ .

☐ people were asked altogether.

3 Complete these sentences. Use the pictograms to help you.

Favourite type of book

Year 3 children

Type	Number of children
comedy	☐☐☐
animal	☐
magical	☐☐
history	☐☐☐
sci-fi	☐☐☐☐

Key: Each ☐ represents 5.

Year 2 children

Type	Number of children
comedy	☐☐☐☐☐☐☐☐☐
animal	☐☐☐☐☐☐
magical	☐☐☐☐☐☐☐
history	☐☐☐☐☐
sci-fi	☐☐

Key: Each ☐ represents 2.

a) ☐ children like comedy in total.

b) ☐ more Year 3 than Year 2 children like history books.

c) ☐ more Year 2 than Year 3 children like animal books.

4 The table shows the holiday destinations of 160 people.

Holiday destination	Europe	Caribbean	USA	UK
Number of people	70	5	25	60

Richard draws a pictogram for the information.

Destination	Number of people
Europe	🧳🧳🧳🧳🧳🧳 ☀
Caribbean	🧳🧳🧳🧳🧳
USA	🧳🧳🧳
UK	🧳 🧳 🧳 🧳 🧳 🧳

Find the mistakes that Richard has made.

_____

_____

_____

_____

Reflect

Write down three things you must remember when you draw a pictogram.

- _____
- _____
-

→ Textbook 3B p100

Bar charts

1 Fairview Animal Rescue counted all the animals in their centre and put the results in a bar chart.

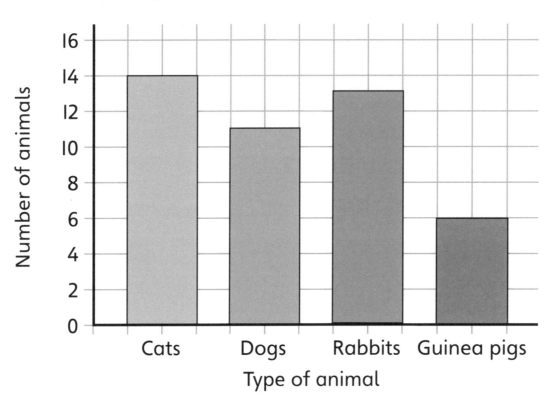

Animals at Fairview Animal Rescue

a) How many cats are in the centre?

The top of the cat bar is level with ☐ .

There are ☐ cats in the centre.

b) How many rabbits are in the centre?

The top of the rabbit bar is half-way between ☐ and ☐ .

There are ☐ rabbits in the centre.

c) How many dogs are in the centre?

There are ☐ dogs in the centre.

2 Complete the sentences.

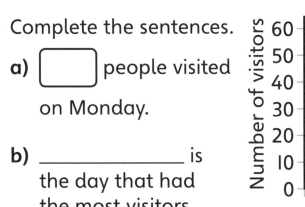

Visits to the animal rescue centre

a) ☐ people visited on Monday.

b) _____ is the day that had the most visitors.

There were ☐ visitors on that day.

c) _____ is the day that had the fewest visitors.

There were ☐ visitors on that day.

3 Here are the favourite wild birds of 23 children in a Cub pack.

Draw a bar chart of the results.

Bird	Number of children
Blackbird	5
Chaffinch	3
Robin	9
Wagtail	2
Wren	4

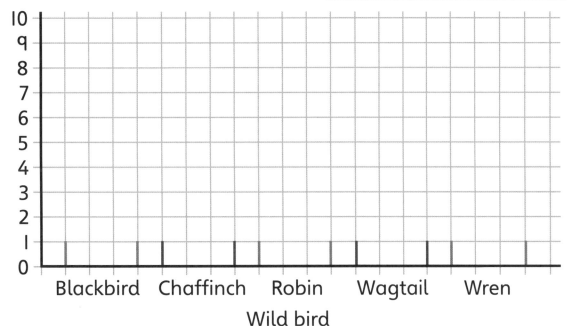

Favourite wild birds

4 Complete the table and chart to show how many animals have been in the centre for each number of weeks.

1 week	☐ animals
2 weeks	55 animals
3 weeks	35 animals
4 weeks	☐ animals

Time taken for animals to be found a home

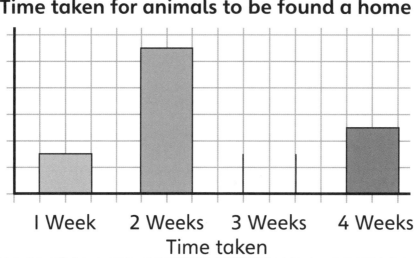

Reflect

Max says, 'Baxter has 10 more people sponsoring him than any other animal.' Is Max right? Explain.

Sponsorship of Fairview animals

Bar charts ❷

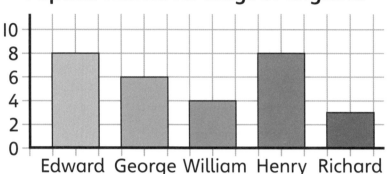

Popular names for kings of England

1 This bar chart shows the five most popular names for kings of England.

a) How many more kings have been called Henry than have been called William?

☐ − ☐ = ☐

☐ more kings have been called Henry than have been called William.

b) Complete the sentences.

☐ more kings have been called George than have been called Richard.

_____ and _____ were the most popular names for kings.

2 a) How many kings were called either Edward or Richard?

☐ + ☐ = ☐

b) Alex says, 'More kings were called Henry than were called Richard and William put together.'

Is she correct? Explain your answer.

_____

_____

3 This bar chart represents the families of the kings and queens of England between 1399 and 1901.

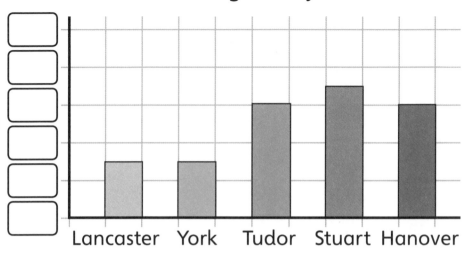

Houses of the kings and queens 1399–1901

Lancaster   York   Tudor   Stuart   Hanover

a) There were 6 Hanover kings and queens.

Complete the bar chart.

b) How many Stuart kings and queens were there? There were

Stuart kings and queens.

4 A newspaper asked some adults and children if they thought Britain should still have a king or queen. They put the results in two bar charts.

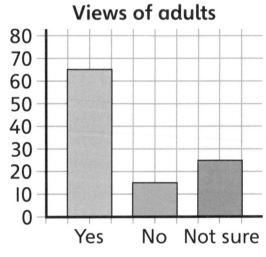

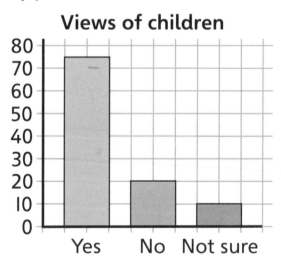

Complete these sentences.

a) more children voted yes compared with adults.

b) people in total were not sure.

c) The newspaper asked children in total.

5 This bar chart shows the length of reign of four kings.

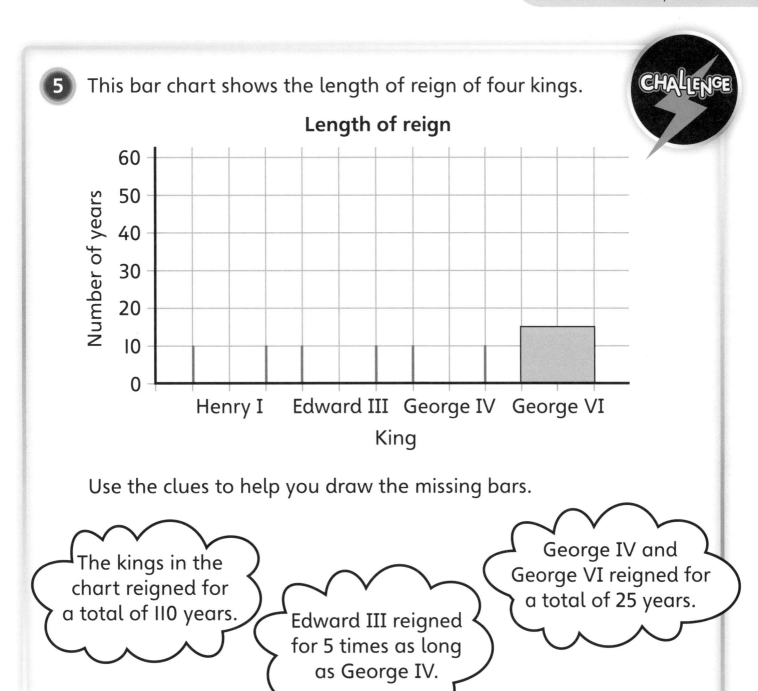

CHALLENGE

Use the clues to help you draw the missing bars.

The kings in the chart reigned for a total of 110 years.

Edward III reigned for 5 times as long as George IV.

George IV and George VI reigned for a total of 25 years.

Reflect

Bella says, 'Bar charts are better than pictograms for presenting information.'

Do you agree? Discuss your reasons with your partner.

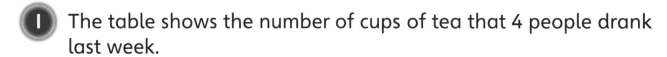

→ Textbook 3B p108

Tables

1 The table shows the number of cups of tea that 4 people drank last week.

	Tom	Becky	Louise	Kieron
Tea (cups)	21	12	18	17

Order the people by the number of cups of tea they drank.

Start with the person who drank the most.

_____

2 The table shows the amount of water they drank in the same week.

	Tom	Becky	Louise	Kieron
Water (glasses)	35	55	38	47

a) Which person drank the most glasses of water?

_____ drank the most glasses of water.

b) How many glasses of water did Becky and Louise drink in total?

Becky and Louise drank ☐ glasses of water in total.

c) Tom drank the same amount of water each day.

How many glasses did he drink each day?

He drank ☐ glasses each day.

d) How many more glasses of water did Becky drink than Kieron?

Becky drank ☐ more glasses of water than Kieron.

3 This table shows the heights of three children at different points in the year.

	January	July	December
Alysia	122 cm	130 cm	132 cm
Noah	121 cm	127 cm	133 cm
Adam	128 cm	132 cm	140 cm

Complete the sentences.

a) _____ was the tallest child in January.

_____ was the shortest child in January.

b) _____ was the tallest child in December.

_____ was the shortest child in December.

c) Noah grew ⬚ cm between January and July.

d) The difference between the heights of Alysia and Adam in December is ⬚ cm.

4 Mrs Dean's class rolled different balls down a ramp made of wood and sand.

They measured the distances the balls rolled.

	Tennis ball	Squash ball	Golf ball
Wood	120 cm		
Sand	90 cm		

The squash ball travels less far than the tennis ball on wood, but further than the tennis ball on sand.

The golf ball travels the furthest distance on wood and the least distance on sand.

Work out some numbers that could go into the table.

Complete the table.

5 Use the information given in the table, bar chart and pictogram to fill in the missing information.

Amount of money spent each week

Family	Food	Non food	Total
Morgan	£	£	£95
Tan	£	£	£120
Agg	£	£	£110

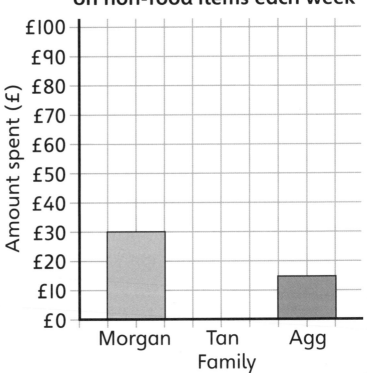

Amount spent on non-food items

Family	Amount
Morgan	
Tan	○○○○○○
Agg	○○○

Key: Each ○ represents £5.

Amount three families spend on non-food items each week

Reflect

Reena says that tables are more useful than pictograms or bar charts for presenting information.

Talk to your partner. Do you agree with Reena? Explain your answer.

End of unit check

My journal

1 The pictogram shows how many ice creams Izzy sold in one day.

Izzy says, 'I sold 5 more caramel ice creams than vanilla.'

Is Izzy correct?

Explain your answer.

The number of ice creams sold in a day

strawberry	🍦🍦🍦🍦
raspberry	🍦🍦🍦
vanilla	🍦🍦🍦
caramel	🍦🍦🍦🍦

Key: 🍦 = 10 ice creams.

_____

_____

2 Write three sentences about the information in the pictogram.

_____

_____

_____

Power check

How do you feel about your work in this unit?

Power puzzle

1 Class 3A collected information about their favourite type of fruit.

Some of the labels are missing from the bar chart.

Use the information on the chart and the clues below to help you complete it.

Class 3A's favourite type of fruit

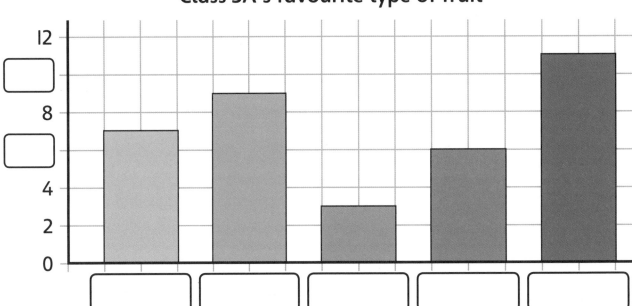

Raspberry is the most popular fruit.

Twice as many people like strawberry best as like kiwi best.

Banana is the second most popular fruit.

The number of people whose favourite fruit is apple is less than 8.

2 Create a pictogram using the information from the bar chart.

Remember to decide how many children each of your symbols will stand for.

raspberry	
strawberry	
kiwi	
banana	
apple	

Key: _____ = _____

Ask your classmates about their favourite type of fruit. Then create a bar graph and pictogram showing the information. Can you think of an efficient way to collect the information?

→ **Textbook 3B p116**

Measuring length

1 **a)** How long is the shark?

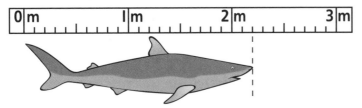

The shark is ⬚ m ⬚ cm long.

b) How long is the dolphin?

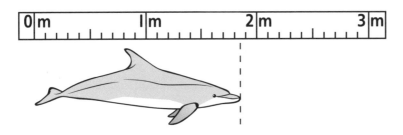

The dolphin is ⬚ m ⬚ cm long.

c) How long is the swordfish?

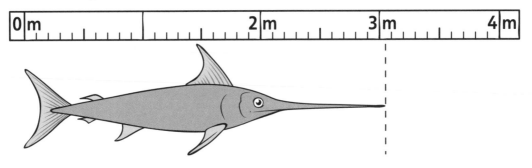

The swordfish is ⬚ m ⬚ cm long.

d) A fish is 95 cm long. Mark its length on the ruler below.

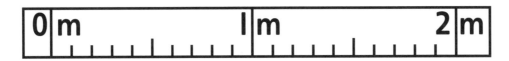

2 Measure the arm span of three people in your class.

Name	Arm span

Arm span

3 Mark has measured the line as 60 cm. Explain his mistake.

0 1 2 3 4 5 6 7 8 9 10 11 12 13 14 15 16 17 18 19 20 21 22 23 24 25 26 27 28 29 30 cm   0 1 2 3 4 5 6 7 8 9 10 11 12 13 14 15 16 17 18 19 20 21 22 23 24 25 26 27 28 29 30 cm

_____

_____

_____

_____

4 Draw arrows to mark these measurements.

a) 50 cm

b) 1 m 10 cm

c) 1 m 90 cm

d) 2 m 75 cm

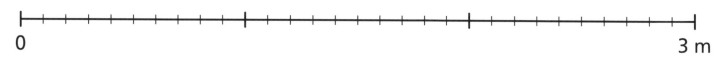

0   3 m

5 Find things in your classroom that are these lengths. Complete the table.

	Item	Length
Under 1 m		
Between 1 m and 1 m 50 cm		
Between 2 m and 3 m		

6 Ebo thinks the line he has drawn on the playground is 1 m 10 cm long.
How could he check?

CHALLENGE

_____

_____

_____

Reflect

How could you accurately measure your height?

_____

_____

_____

Measuring length ②

1 What measurements are shown?

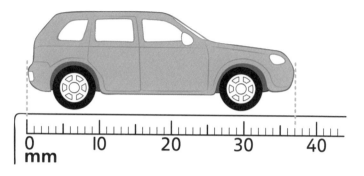

Not shown actual size

a) The toy car is ☐ mm.

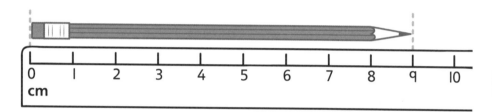

Not shown actual size

b) The pencil is ☐ cm.

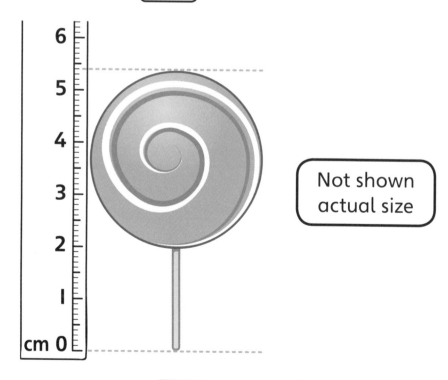

Not shown actual size

c) The lollipop is ☐ cm and ☐ mm.

89

2 Use a ruler to draw lines that measure:

a) 3 cm   b) 56 mm   c) 4 cm and 8 mm

3 What lengths are shown?

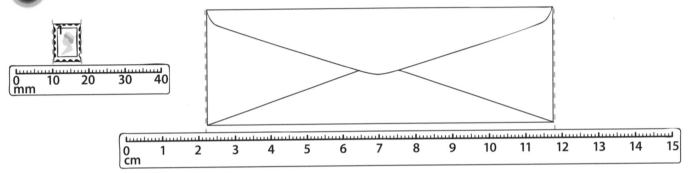

The stamp is ⬚ mm.

The envelope is ⬚ cm and ⬚ mm.

How could you make these easier to measure? _____

_____

4 Measure these objects using a ruler.

Write the measurements in cm and mm.

Object		
Pencil	⬚ cm	⬚ mm
Book	⬚ cm	⬚ mm
Glue stick	⬚ cm	⬚ mm
Rubber	⬚ cm	⬚ mm

5 **a)** Andy wants to measure the lengths of an elephant and a mouse. Explain which units of measure he should use for each animal and why.

CHALLENGE

I think Andy could use metres, centimetres or millimetres!

_____

_____

_____

_____

b) List some other items you could measure in metres or centimetres.

Metres	Centimetres

Reflect

Explain how to measure accurately using cm and mm.

To measure accurately you must _____

_____

_____

→ **Textbook 3B p124**

Equivalent lengths – metres and centimetres

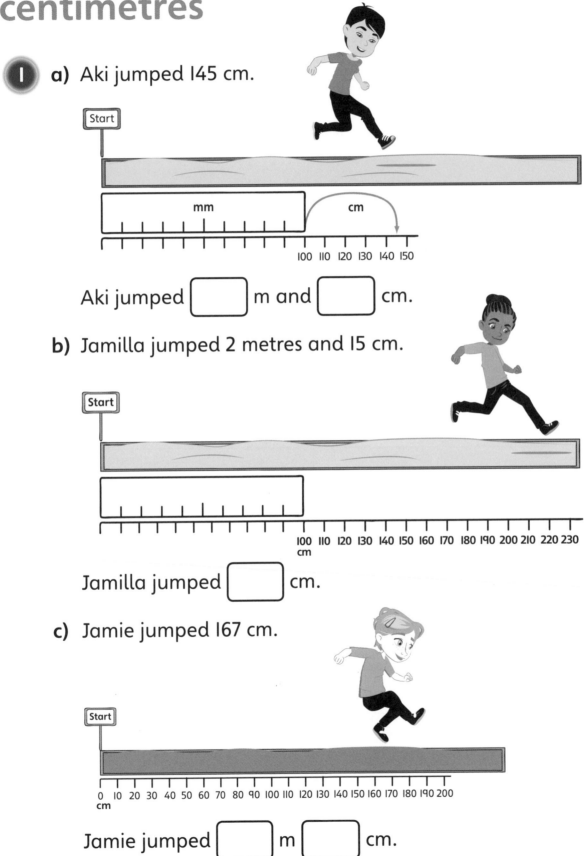

1 **a)** Aki jumped 145 cm.

Aki jumped [ ] m and [ ] cm.

b) Jamilla jumped 2 metres and 15 cm.

Jamilla jumped [ ] cm.

c) Jamie jumped 167 cm.

Jamie jumped [ ] m [ ] cm.

2 Complete the part-whole models.

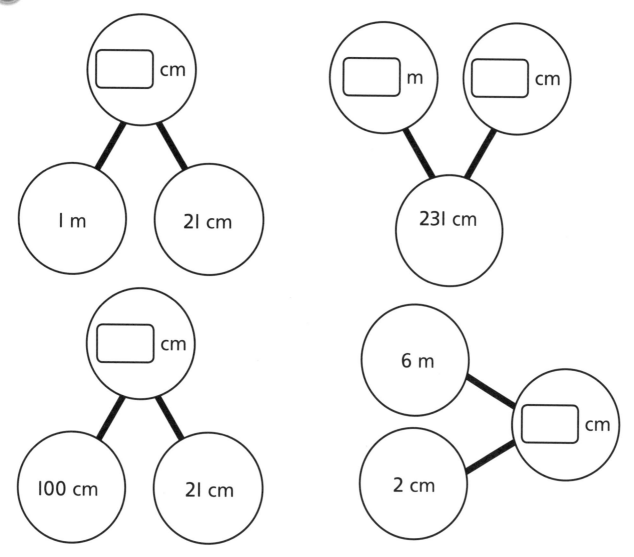

3 Complete the table.

5 m 30 cm	[ ] cm
[ ] m [ ] cm	673 cm
3 m 3 cm	[ ] cm
0 m 23 cm	[ ] cm

4 Andy says 2 m 4 cm is 240 cm. Explain why this is wrong.

_____

_____

_____

5 Play this game with a partner. Take turns.

Choose a box, and say the length in centimetres.

If you say it correctly, draw a line through it.

The first player to get four boxes lined up (in a row, a column or diagonally) wins.

5 m 32 cm	0 m 10 cm	7 m 64 cm	0 m 0 cm
3 m 43 cm	5 m 74 cm	9 m 32 cm	0 m 75 cm
0 m 26 cm	3 m 12 cm	1 m 10 cm	8 m 46 cm
0 m 56 cm	4 m 7 cm	0 m 1 cm	3 m
6 m 32 cm	0 m 45 cm	3 m 65 cm	0 m 64 cm

Reflect

3 m

7 m 22 cm

243 cm

Pick a measurement and explain how to convert it to the equivalent length.

_____

_____

_____

Equivalent lengths – centimetres and millimetres

1 Luis wants to cut some string.

He needs some help measuring.

(The rulers are not shown actual size.)

a) Mark 2 cm 5 mm on the ruler.

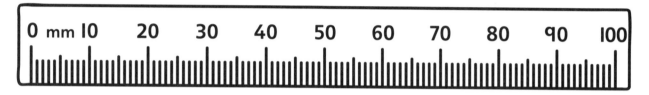

b) Mark 30 mm on the ruler.

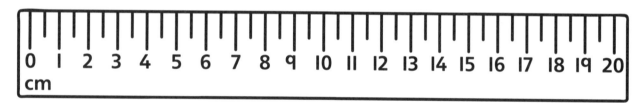

c) Mark 9 cm 9 mm on the ruler.

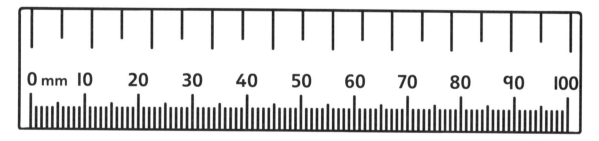

d) Mark 1 mm on the ruler.

2 Complete the part-whole models.

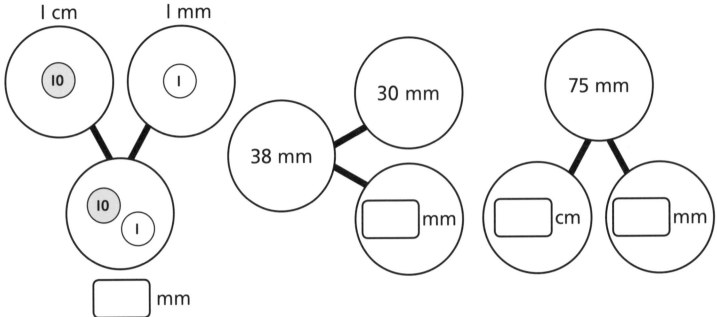

I cm

I mm

10

1

10

1

☐ mm

38 mm

30 mm

☐ mm

75 mm

☐ cm

☐ mm

3 Complete this table.

> I need to be careful with my place value in these questions.

7 cm 22 mm	☐ mm
☐ cm ☐ mm	92 mm
3 cm 0 mm	☐ cm
2 cm 81 mm	☐ mm

4 Measure the lengths of three items from your pencil case.

Write the answers in mm and also in cm and mm.

a) Item: _____ ☐ mm, ☐ cm and ☐ mm

b) Item: _____ ☐ mm, ☐ cm and ☐ mm

c) Item: _____ ☐ mm, ☐ cm and ☐ mm

5 Kate says there are no whole centimetres in 5 mm.

Is she correct? Explain.

_____

_____

_____

_____

6 Work with a partner. Try to cut strips of paper that are exactly these lengths:

CHALLENGE

a) 67 mm

d) 121 mm

b) 9 cm 2 mm

e) 8 cm 9 mm

c) 6 cm 7 mm

Which two lengths are equal? _____ and _____

Reflect

Luis measures a really long piece of string. He writes down 765 mm. He then converts it to 76 cm 5 mm.

Is it better to use millimetres or centimetres and millimetres for longer lengths? Why?

I think _____ are better

because _____

_____

→ Textbook 3B p132

Comparing lengths

 a) Mark on the ruler below where the four paper aeroplanes landed.

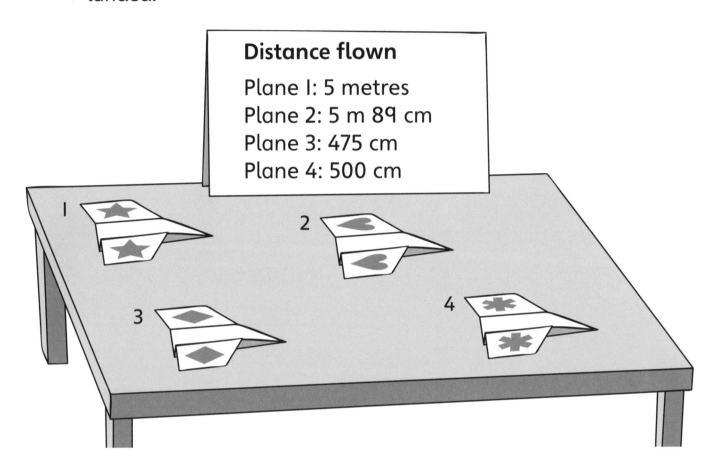

Distance flown

Plane 1: 5 metres
Plane 2: 5 m 89 cm
Plane 3: 475 cm
Plane 4: 500 cm

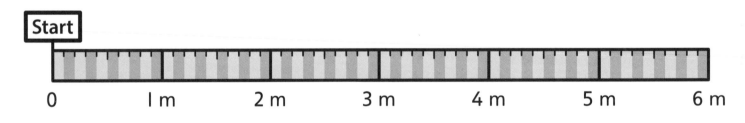

b) Which aeroplane flew the furthest? Plane ☐

c) Which aeroplane flew the shortest distance? Plane ☐

d) Which aeroplane flew between 4 and 5 metres? Plane ☐

2 Write the following lengths in ascending order from shortest to longest.

200 cm   970 mm   1 m 95 cm   1 m 90 mm   190 cm

_____   _____   _____   _____   _____

Shortest   Longest

3 Complete these number sentences.

I think I can use the signs < and > to answer some of these.

a) 5 m 87 cm ◯ 495 cm

b) 8 m 240 mm ◯ 8 m 25 cm

c) 402 cm = _____ m and _____ mm

4

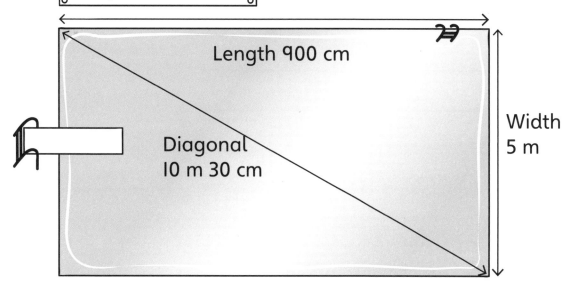

Swimming pool
Depth 130 cm

Length 900 cm

Diagonal
10 m 30 cm

Width
5 m

Complete these number sentences.

a) The longest distance you can swim in a straight line is

☐ m and ☐ cm.

b) The shortest distance from one corner of the pool to another is

☐ cm.

99

5 Which is longer, the pencil case or the folder?

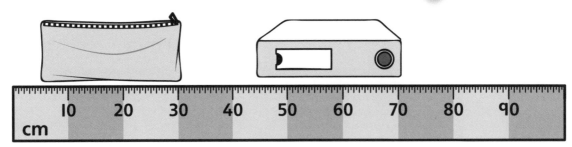

The _____ is longer.

6 I m 35 cm < _____ cm < I m 370 mm.

Do you agree with Astrid that this cannot be solved?

Explain your answer.

_____

_____

_____

_____

 CHALLENGE

This cannot be solved because it mixes metres, centimetres and millimetres.

Reflect

How would you order the lengths 3 m 8 cm, 380 cm and 380 mm?

Adding lengths

1 A carpenter joins two pieces of wood together. What is the total length?

a)

 6 m

3 m

6 m + 3 m = ☐ m

b)

 40 cm

20 cm

40 cm + 20 cm = ☐ cm

2 A plumber joins pieces of pipe together. What is the total length?

 120 cm

65 cm

120 cm + 65 cm = _____

3 A shop makes a display by putting a vase on a stand. What is the total height of the display?

The total height is _____ .

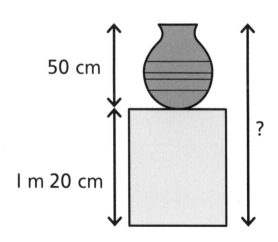

50 cm

1 m 20 cm

?

4 The shop has more displays of vases and stands. Complete the table.

Display	Stand Height	Vase Height	Total Height
A	40 cm	30 cm	
B	80 cm	30 cm	
C	1 m 20 cm	60 cm	
D	1 m 30 cm	70 cm	

5 Complete the number sentences.

a) 75 cm + 25 cm = ☐ m

c) 6 cm + 70 mm = ☐ cm

b) 27 mm + ☐ mm = 3 cm

d) 2 m 25 cm + ☐ cm = 3 m

6 Jamilla and Andy took part in the final of a hop, skip and jump competition.

Jamilla hopped 80 cm, skipped 70 cm and jumped 1 m 20 cm.

Andy hopped 70 cm, skipped 1 m 10 cm and jumped 1 m.

Who won the competition?

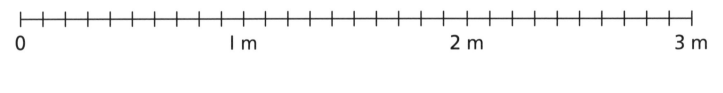

0   1 m   2 m   3 m

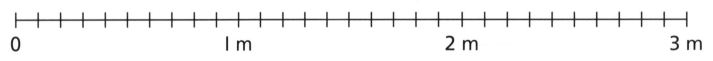

0   1 m   2 m   3 m

_____ won.

7 These four books are stacked on top of each other. What is the total height of the stack of books?

The total height of the stack of books is _____ .

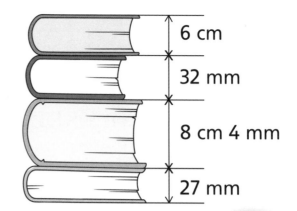

6 cm

32 mm

8 cm 4 mm

27 mm

8 Mrs Dean asked Zac to work out the total length of two display boards.

CHALLENGE

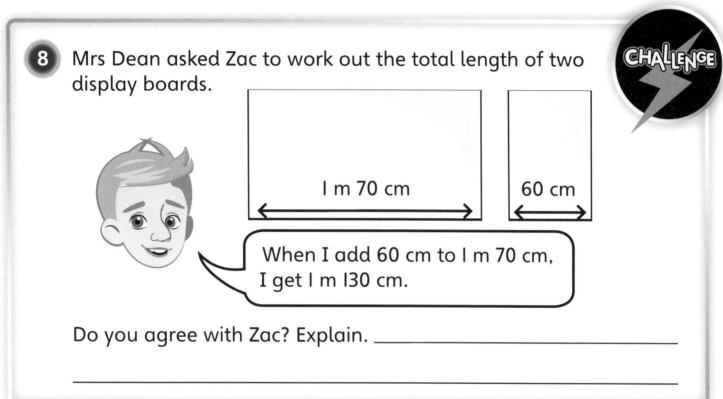

1 m 70 cm

60 cm

When I add 60 cm to 1 m 70 cm, I get 1 m 130 cm.

Do you agree with Zac? Explain. _____

_____

Reflect

Richard knits a scarf that is 1 m 80 cm long. He knits another 30 cm. How long is the scarf now? Explain your steps.

→ Textbook 3B p140

Subtracting lengths

1 **a)** The pipe was 3 m 50 cm long. Jen has cut a 1 m piece off the end. How long is the pipe now?

3 m 50 cm

1 m

The pipe is now _____ long.

b) Emma's painting was 1 m 5 cm long. She has cut off 95 mm to make it fit a frame. How long is the painting now?

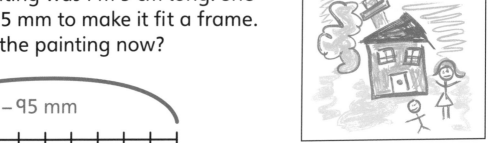

– 95 mm

95 cm   1 m   1 m 5 cm

Emma's painting is _____ long.

c) Toshi has a plank 3 m 50 cm long. He needs a piece 2 m long. How much should he cut off the plank?

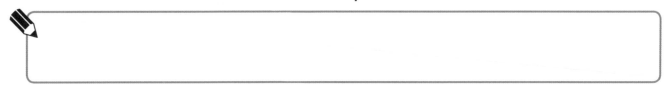

Toshi should cut _____ off the plank.

d) A piece of string is 65 mm long. Aki cuts off 3 cm. How long is the string now?

The string is now _____ long.

2 Sofia puts a flower in a vase.

The vase is 1 m 20 cm high, and the flower is 1 m 40 cm high.

How far does the flower stick out above the vase?

The flower sticks out ⬚ cm.

1 m 40 cm high

?

1 m 20 cm high

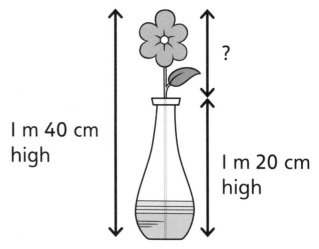

3 **a)** 1 m 10 cm – 50 cm = ⬚

e) 85 mm – 2 cm = ⬚

b) 2 m 10 cm – 50 cm = ⬚

f) 5 cm 8 mm – 20 mm = ⬚

c) 310 cm – 1 m 50 cm = ⬚

g) 2 cm 5 mm – 8 mm = ⬚

d) 350 cm – ⬚ = 2 m 10 cm

h) 120 mm – ⬚ = 6 cm

4 Reena bought a new 10 m reel of ribbon, and used 2 m 50 cm of it.

She then lent the reel to her friend Aki.

When Aki gave the reel back, there was 3 m 60 cm of ribbon left.

How much ribbon did Aki use?

CHALLENGE

Aki used _____ .

Reflect

What method could you use to solve each of these subtractions?

3 m 30 cm – 165 cm   2 m – 1 m 30 cm

Measuring the perimeter

1 **a)** Ebo has measured the bottom side of this shape as 4 cm.

What are the lengths of the other sides?

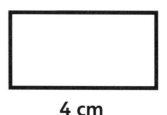

The other sides have a length of

☐ cm, ☐ cm and ☐ cm.

4 cm

What is the perimeter of the rectangle?

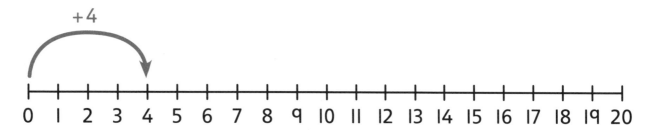

The perimeter of the rectangle is ☐ cm.

b) Measure the perimeter of the triangle.

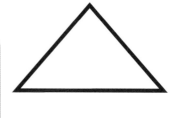

The perimeter of the triangle is ☐ cm.

c) Measure the perimeter of the square.

The square has a perimeter of ☐ cm.

107

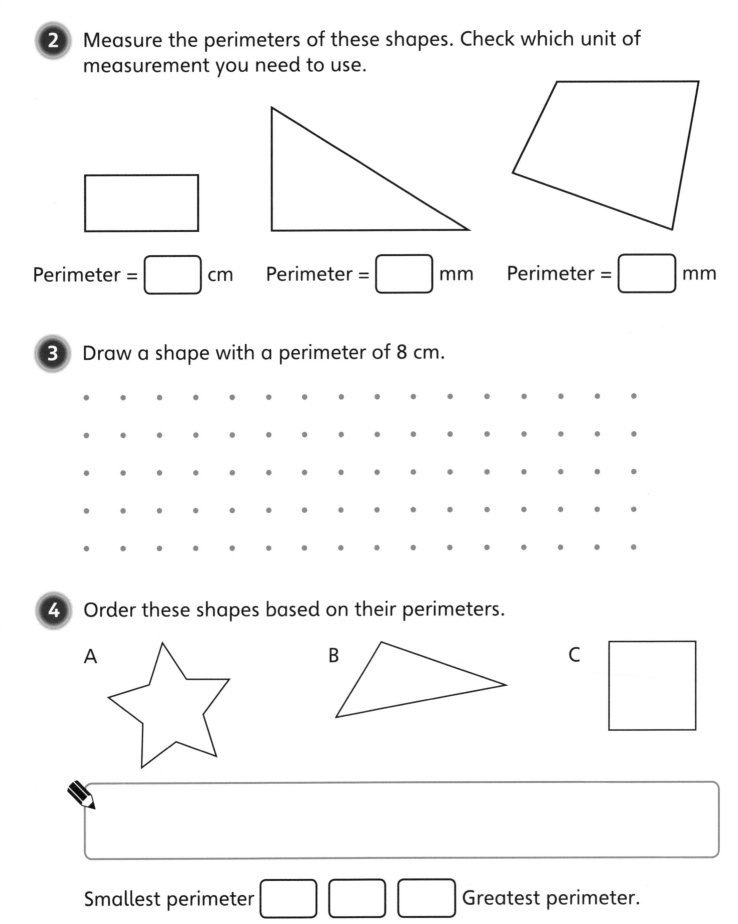

2 Measure the perimeters of these shapes. Check which unit of measurement you need to use.

Perimeter = ☐ cm   Perimeter = ☐ mm   Perimeter = ☐ mm

3 Draw a shape with a perimeter of 8 cm.

4 Order these shapes based on their perimeters.

A

B

C

Smallest perimeter ☐ ☐ ☐ Greatest perimeter.

5 Olivia has been asked to draw shapes with perimeters of 10 cm.

Help Olivia complete the shapes below.

> I think I am going to use subtraction to help me solve these problems.

| Perimeter = 10 cm |

| Perimeter = 10 cm |

Reflect

Andy says that only a triangle could have a perimeter of 12 cm. Is he correct? How do you know?

→ Textbook 3B p148

Measuring the perimeter ②

1 Jen needs to put a fence around the perimeter of her fields. Help her work out the perimeter of each field.

a)

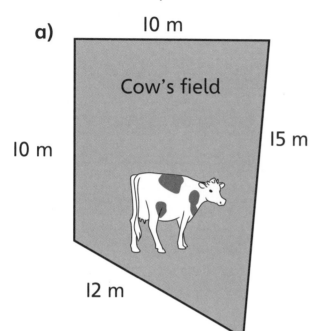

10 m

Cow's field

10 m

15 m

12 m

The perimeter of the cow's field is ☐ metres.

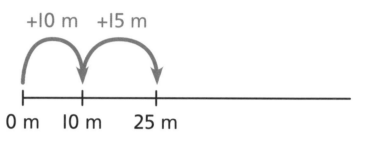

+10 m   +15 m

0 m   10 m   25 m

b) The perimeter of the sheep's field is ☐ metres.

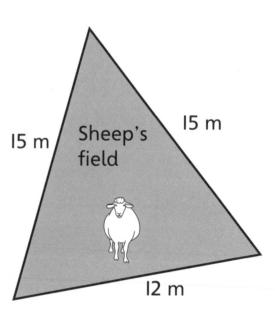

15 m   Sheep's field

15 m

12 m

c)

12 m

Goat's field

5 m

8 m

3 m

3 m

15 m

The perimeter of the goat's field is ☐ metres.

2 Complete the missing side lengths for the fields below.

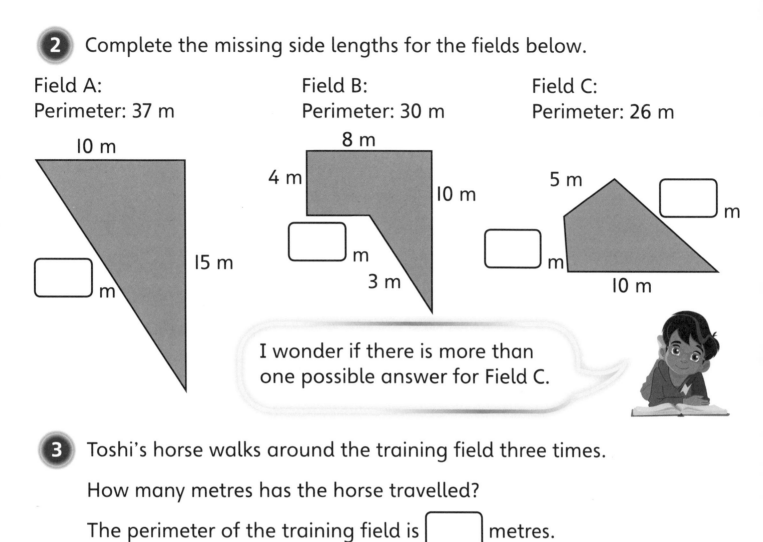

Field A:
Perimeter: 37 m

10 m

15 m

☐ m

Field B:
Perimeter: 30 m

8 m

4 m

10 m

☐ m

3 m

Field C:
Perimeter: 26 m

5 m

☐ m

☐ m

10 m

I wonder if there is more than one possible answer for Field C.

3 Toshi's horse walks around the training field three times.

How many metres has the horse travelled?

The perimeter of the training field is ☐ metres.

The horse has travelled

☐ metres.

I need to work out 3 times the perimeter.

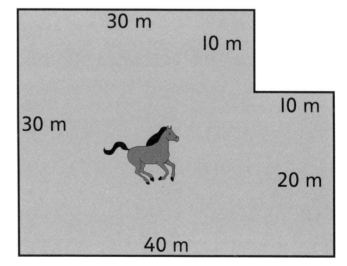

30 m

10 m

10 m

30 m

20 m

40 m

III

4 Draw lines to match the items below with their most likely perimeter.

| A piece of A4 paper |
| An interactive whiteboard |
| A premiership football field |
| A £5 note |

| 420 m |
| 526 cm |
| 380 mm |
| 101 cm |

I wonder what units I should use to measure each item.

CHALLENGE

5 Jen has 32 m of fence. One of the sides of her enclosure must be 12 m long.

Sketch and label two different sized enclosures she could make, using all 32 m of fence.

Reflect

Explain how you can work out the perimeter of any shape if you know the lengths of the sides.

Problem solving – length

1 Luis swims 3 lengths of 25 metres each. How far does he swim?

25 m	25 m	25 m

?

$25 \times \boxed{} = \boxed{}$. Luis swims $\boxed{}$ metres.

2 Emma cuts a 90 cm ribbon into 5 equal pieces. How long is each piece?

90 cm

$\boxed{} \div \boxed{} = \boxed{}$

Each piece is $\boxed{}$ cm.

3 A pastry has 9 cm of cream piped onto it. A baker can pipe 72 cm of cream in one minute. How many pastries is that?

$\boxed{} \div \boxed{} = \boxed{}$

The baker pipes $\boxed{}$ pastries in one minute.

113

4 How much fence is needed to go all the way around the square school field?

40 m

Write the calculation you used.

_____

[ ] metres of fence is needed.

5 Jamilla is making 4 curtain poles. She needs 3 poles that are 1 m 45 cm and one pole that is 2 m 45 cm. How much curtain pole does she need in total?

Draw a picture to show this. Then solve the problem.

Jamilla needs [ ] m [ ] cm of curtain pole.

6 Which is longer: 5 × 35 cm or 3 × 53 cm?

Draw a diagram to show your method. Then write your answer.

_____ is longer.

7 Ebo cuts these pieces of string in half. Write the missing lengths.

CHALLENGE

3 m

☐ cm

☐ cm

33 cm

☐ cm ☐ mm   ☐ cm ☐ mm

1 m 33 cm

☐ cm ☐ mm   ☐ cm ☐ mm

Reflect

Tick the two calculations you would need to do to solve this problem.

Susan buys 3 hose pipes. Each hose pipe is 3 m 60 cm metres long. How much hose pipe does she buy?

3 + 60 = 63 ☐   9 × 3 = 27 ☐

60 cm × 3 = 180 cm ☐   3 m × 3 = 9 m ☐

→ **Textbook 3B p156**

Problem solving – length ❷

① A chocolate bar is made up of 8 small pieces.

Each small piece is 20 mm wide and 30 mm long.

What is the width and length of the whole chocolate bar?

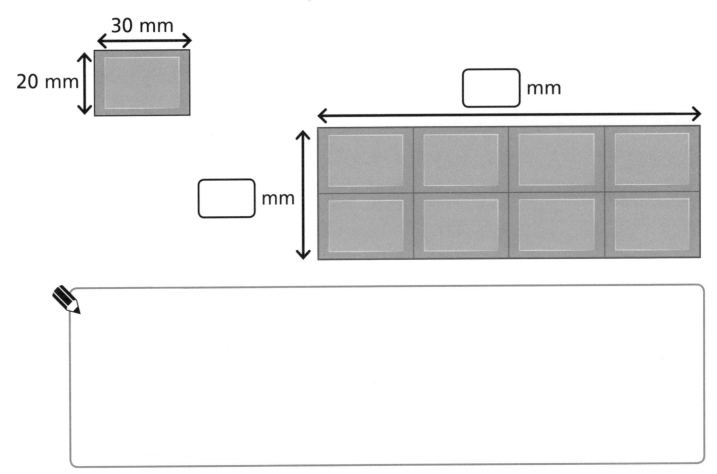

30 mm

20 mm

☐ mm

☐ mm

② Bella has 60 cm of ribbon. She uses 24 cm then 95 mm.

How much ribbon does she have left?

60 cm

24 cm		?

Bella has ☐ mm of ribbon left.

3 A tower has 6 storeys of 4 m 50 cm each and a roof of 3 m 27 cm.

What is the total height of the tower?

The tower is ☐ m and ☐ cm high.

4 Amal walks his dog 55 m every minute for 5 minutes. Holly walks her dog 60 m every minute for 4 minutes. How much further do Amal and his dog walk?

Amal

55 m	55 m	55 m	55 m	55 m

Holly

60 m	60 m	60 m	60 m	?

☐ − ☐ = ☐

Amal and his dog walk

☐ m further.

5 Blue bricks are 5 cm tall and yellow bricks are 8 cm tall.

Geoff builds a tower with 2 blue bricks and 4 yellow bricks.

What bricks does he need to add to his tower to make it 60 cm tall?

Geoff needs ☐ blue bricks and ☐ yellow bricks.

6 Look at the measurements of this rectangle.

3 cm

The rectangle has been used twice to make this shape:

7 cm 5 mm

What is the perimeter of the shape?

The perimeter is ☐ cm and ☐ mm.

What perimeters could you make with three of these rectangles?

Reflect

What new things have you learnt in this unit on length? Explain to your partner what you felt was the most important part of the unit and why.

End of unit check

My journal

1. Reena and Danny want to know if their combined height is greater than the combined height of Richard and Ambika.

   Complete the bar models. Show your working out.

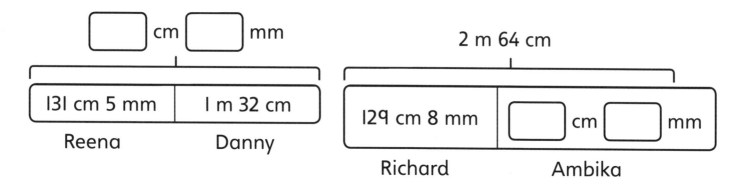

Work out which two children have the greater combined height.

The combined height of _____ and _____ >

the combined height of _____ and _____ .

2 Max measures the perimeter of a rectangular sheet of paper.

30 cm

20 cm

Max cuts the paper in half. He thinks the perimeter will be halved too.

Is Max correct? Explain your answer. Use the key words below to help you.

_____

_____

_____

_____

_____

_____

_____

Key words

sides, perimeter, length, width, square, centimetre, rectangle

Power check

How do you feel about your work in this unit?

Power puzzle

A rectangle has a total perimeter of 36 cm. What could the lengths of its sides be? Find four possible answers.

Length of rectangle	Width of rectangle	Draw what you think it might look like

Try the puzzle again, this time for a rectangle with a total perimeter of 48 cm.

→ Textbook 3B p164

Unit and non-unit fractions

1 Complete the sentences.

There are ⬚ birds altogether.

The denominator is ⬚ .

⬚ birds are flying to the right.

The numerator is ⬚ .

$\dfrac{⬚}{⬚}$ of the birds are flying to the right.

2 Match each shape to the fraction that shows how much of the shape is shaded.

$\dfrac{1}{4}$

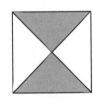

$\dfrac{2}{3}$

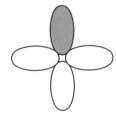

$\dfrac{1}{2}$

3 Complete the sentences.

$\frac{1}{5}$ of the cars are _____ .

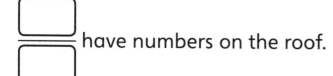 have numbers on the roof.    are _____ .

4 **a)** Divide the bar into 2 equal parts. Shade in $\frac{1}{2}$.

b) Divide the bar into 3 equal parts. Shade in $\frac{1}{3}$.

c) Use your answers to **a)** and **b)** to help complete the following expressions. Use the <, = or > sign for each expression.

$\frac{1}{2}$ ◯ $\frac{1}{3}$ $\frac{1}{3}$ ◯ $\frac{1}{2}$

5 Shade $\frac{1}{2}$ of each of the three large squares. Show $\frac{1}{2}$ in as many different ways as possible. You may find it useful to copy the large squares on to a piece of squared paper.

CHALLENGE

A

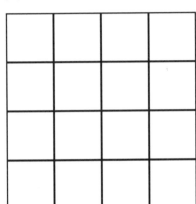

B

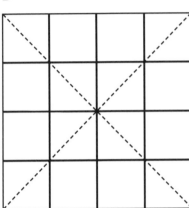

C

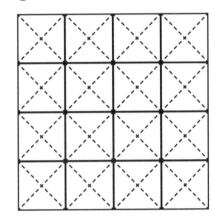

Reflect

Colour the hexagon so that it is $\frac{1}{2}$ yellow and $\frac{1}{6}$ red.

How do you know you have coloured the shape correctly?

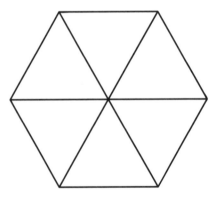

I know that the fraction shaded yellow is a $\frac{1}{2}$ because

I know that the fraction shaded red is a $\frac{1}{6}$ because

Making the whole

1 Complete the missing information.

a) ☐ out of the 6 eggs are in the box.

This is $\dfrac{\square}{\square}$ of the whole.

☐ out of the 6 eggs have been used.

This is $\dfrac{\square}{\square}$ of the whole.

$\dfrac{\square}{\square} + \dfrac{\square}{\square} = 1$

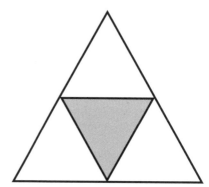

b) ☐ out of the ☐ parts is shaded.

This is $\dfrac{\square}{\square}$ of the whole.

☐ out of the ☐ parts are not shaded.

This is $\dfrac{\square}{\square}$ of the whole.

$\dfrac{\square}{\square} + \dfrac{\square}{\square} = 1$

2 **a)** $\frac{3}{5} + \frac{2}{5} = 1$ whole

Use the bar model to show how you know this is true.

b) $\frac{1}{4} + \frac{3}{4} = 1$

Use the bar model to show how you know this is true.

3 Complete these number sentences.

a) $\frac{5}{8} + \dfrac{\boxed{}}{\boxed{}} = 1$

d) $\frac{7}{7} = \frac{3}{7} + \dfrac{\boxed{}}{\boxed{}}$

b) $\dfrac{\boxed{}}{\boxed{}} = \frac{2}{5} + \frac{3}{5}$

e) $1 = \frac{1}{6} + \dfrac{\boxed{}}{\boxed{}}$

c) $\dfrac{\boxed{}}{\boxed{}} + \frac{1}{9} = \frac{9}{9}$

f) $\frac{4}{9} + \dfrac{\boxed{}}{\boxed{}} = 1$

4 In a group, $\frac{4}{7}$ of the children are sitting down.

What fraction of the group are standing up?

$\dfrac{\boxed{}}{\boxed{}}$ of the group are standing up.

5 Explain the mistake in this calculation.

$\frac{2}{3} + \frac{1}{3} = \frac{3}{6}$

Can you use the words **numerator** and **denominator** in your answer?

_____

_____

_____

_____

6 Write two different ways that you could share the cake between the 2 plates.

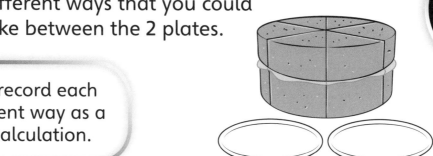

CHALLENGE

I will record each different way as a new calculation.

I whole cake = $\dfrac{\boxed{}}{\boxed{}} + \dfrac{\boxed{}}{\boxed{}}$ I whole cake = $\dfrac{\boxed{}}{\boxed{}} + \dfrac{\boxed{}}{\boxed{}}$

Reflect

What did you learn about making the whole in today's lesson?

Today I learnt that _____

_____

_____

→ Textbook 3B p172

Tenths

1 What fraction of each shape is shaded?

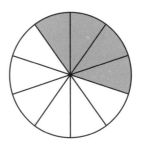

a) $\dfrac{\boxed{}}{10}$ of the circle is shaded.

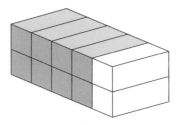

b) $\dfrac{\boxed{}}{10}$ of the cuboid is shaded.

c) $\dfrac{\boxed{}}{\boxed{}}$ of the smiley faces are shaded.

2 Colour the correct fractions.

a) Colour $\frac{4}{10}$ of the triangles.

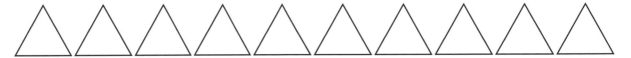

b) Colour $\frac{7}{10}$ of the rectangle.

c) Colour the circles. Leave $\frac{2}{10}$ of the circles white.

3 2 tickets have been taken off a strip of 10 tickets.

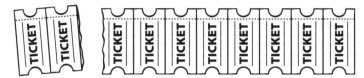

a) What fraction of the 10 tickets are left? $\dfrac{\square}{\square}$ are left.

b) Use the number line to show the fraction of tickets that have been taken off and the fraction of tickets that are left.

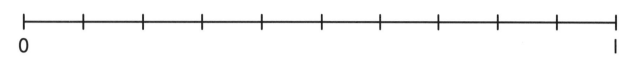

0   1

4 Complete the calculations. Show each one on a number line.

a) $1 = \dfrac{1}{10} + \dfrac{\square}{\square}$

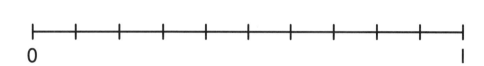

0   1

b) $\dfrac{\square}{\square} + \dfrac{3}{10} = \dfrac{10}{10}$

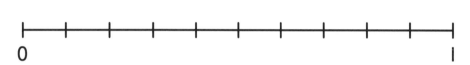

0   1

5 Richard and Jamilla are both counting in tenths.

Richard starts at 0 and counts up. Jamilla starts at 1 and counts down.

If they both count at the same speed will they ever say the same fraction at the same time?

Explain your answer.

_____

_____

_____

6 This strip of paper is $\frac{1}{10}$ of the whole.

Explain what shape the whole could have been. Is there more than one possibility?

_____

_____

7 Lexi has been experimenting to see how many different ways she can make a whole using tenths.

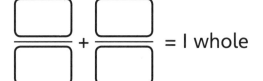 = 1 whole

How many different possible ways can you find?

Reflect

What will the next 2 numbers in the sequence be?

I know the next 2 numbers in the sequence will be [ ] and _____

[ ] [ ] because _____

_____

130

Tenths ②

① Shade $\frac{1}{10}$ of each bar model and complete the calculations.

I whole

a) I out of the 10 parts must be shaded. $1 \div 10 = \dfrac{\boxed{}}{\boxed{}}$

b) There are 2 wholes. I out of the 10 parts in each whole must be shaded.

2 wholes

I whole   I whole

Altogether $\boxed{}$ tenths have been shaded. $2 \div 10 = \dfrac{\boxed{}}{\boxed{}}$

c) $3 \div 10 = \dfrac{\boxed{}}{\boxed{}}$

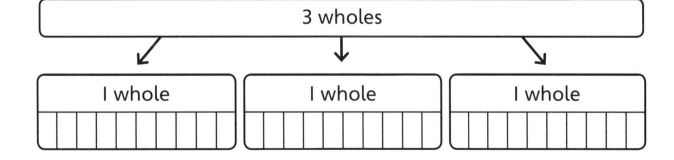

3 wholes

I whole   I whole   I whole

131

d) $5 \div 10 = \dfrac{\boxed{}}{\boxed{}}$

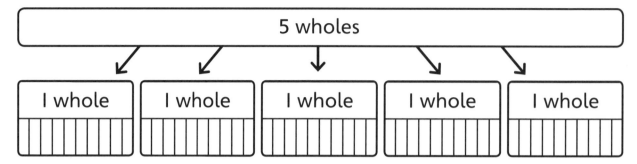

5 wholes

I whole I whole I whole I whole I whole

2 There are 30 grapes in a bag. Each child gets $\frac{1}{10}$ of the bag of grapes.

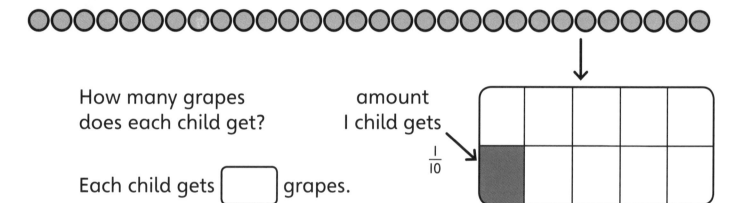

How many grapes does each child get?

amount I child gets

$\frac{1}{10}$

Each child gets $\boxed{}$ grapes.

3 Complete the calculations.

a) $4 \div 10 = \dfrac{\boxed{}}{10}$

b) $5 \div 10 = \dfrac{\boxed{}}{10}$

c) $\dfrac{\boxed{}}{\boxed{}} = 6 \div 10$

d) $7 \div 10 = \dfrac{\boxed{}}{\boxed{}}$

e) $10 \div 10 = \dfrac{\boxed{}}{\boxed{}}$

f) $0 \div 10 = \dfrac{\boxed{}}{\boxed{}}$

4 Complete the calculations.

a) $\boxed{} \div 10 = \frac{2}{10}$

c) $3 \div 10 = \dfrac{\boxed{}}{\boxed{}}$

b) $9 \div \boxed{} = \frac{9}{10}$

d) $\boxed{} \div 10 = \dfrac{\boxed{}}{\boxed{}}$

5 There are 10 children at a party. There are 5 pizzas.

Each child eats $\frac{1}{10}$ of the 5 pizzas.

What fraction of each pizza does each child eat?

How should the pizzas be cut so that this is possible?

 CHALLENGE

I wonder if there is more than one way that this could be solved.

Reflect

Prove that 2 divided by 10 is equal to $\frac{2}{10}$.

I know 2 divided by 10 is equal to $\frac{2}{10}$ because

_____

_____

_____

→ **Textbook 3B p180**

Fractions as numbers

1 Complete the sentences.

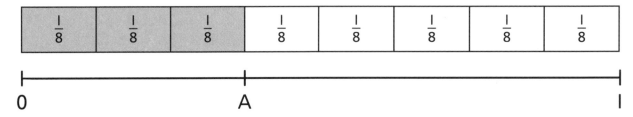

a) The whole has been split into ☐ parts.

Each part is $\dfrac{\square}{\square}$. A represents the number $\dfrac{\square}{\square}$.

b) 1 has been split into ☐ parts.

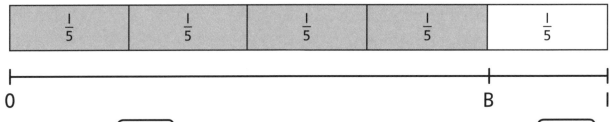

Each part is $\dfrac{\square}{\square}$. B represents the number $\dfrac{\square}{\square}$.

c) 1 has been split into ☐ parts.

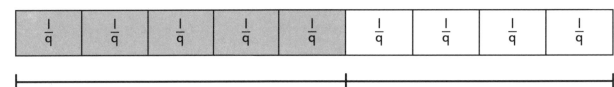

Each part is $\dfrac{\square}{\square}$. C represents the number $\dfrac{\square}{\square}$.

2 What fractions are shown at points A, B and C?

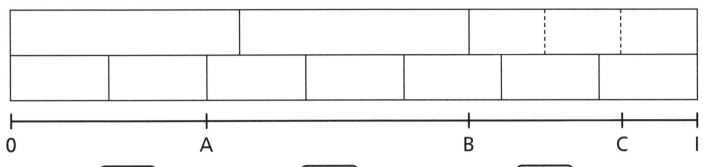

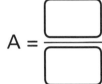 A = ⬜/⬜   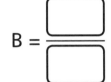 B = ⬜/⬜   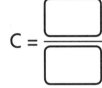 C = ⬜/⬜

3 Mark these fractions in the correct positions on the number lines.

a) $\frac{1}{3}$

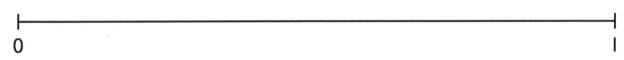

0   1

b) $\frac{4}{8}$

0   1

4 Help Astrid position these fractions on the number line.

$\frac{3}{10}$ $\frac{5}{10}$ $\frac{9}{10}$

0   1

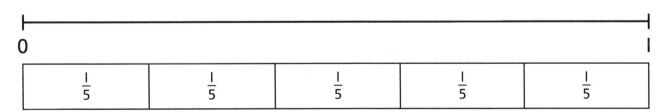

| $\frac{1}{5}$ | $\frac{1}{5}$ | $\frac{1}{5}$ | $\frac{1}{5}$ | $\frac{1}{5}$ |

I do not think I can use the resource that I have been given to help me.

135

5 Explain the mistakes that have been made.

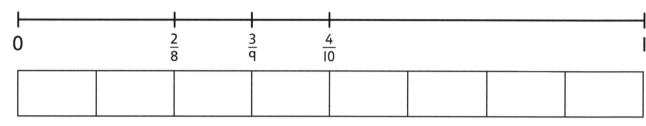

_____

_____

_____

6 Mark $\frac{1}{8}$, $\frac{1}{4}$ and $\frac{1}{2}$ on the number line.

CHALLENGE

0   1

a) What size is the interval between $\frac{1}{8}$ and $\frac{1}{4}$? _____

b) What size is the interval between $\frac{1}{8}$ and $\frac{1}{2}$? _____

Reflect

Complete these sentences.

To place $\frac{1}{5}$ on a number line you must first

_____

and then

_____

To place any fraction on a number line you must first

_____

and then

_____

Fractions as numbers ②

1 Mark the lengths on the number lines.

a) $3\frac{1}{5}$ m

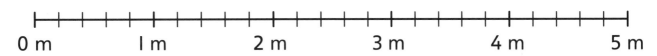

0 m   1 m   2 m   3 m   4 m   5 m

First, I find the whole number ⬚ on the number line.

Then I count on ⬚ fifth.

b) $2\frac{3}{5}$ m

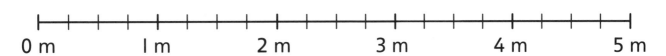

0 m   1 m   2 m   3 m   4 m   5 m

First, I find the whole number ⬚ on the number line.

Then I count on ⬚ fifths.

c) $4\frac{3}{4}$ m

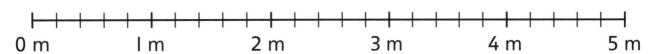

0 m   1 m   2 m   3 m   4 m   5 m

d) $1\frac{2}{3}$ m

0 m   1 m   2 m   3 m   4 m   5 m

2 Mark the fraction shown in each picture on the number line.

a)

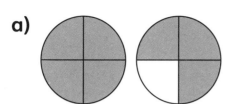

b)

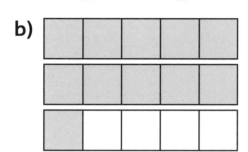

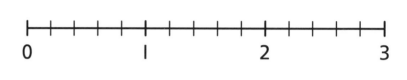

c)

3 What fractions are marked by the letters A, B and C?

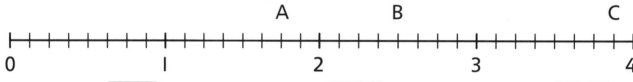

A = ◻ ◻/◻   B = ◻ ◻/◻   C = ◻ ◻/◻

4 Which of these numbers could be represented on the number line by X?

$3\frac{1}{4}$ $2\frac{3}{6}$ $4\frac{7}{8}$ $3\frac{9}{10}$

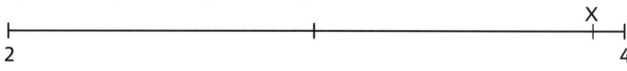

Explain your choice.

_____

_____

CHALLENGE

5 Danny and Aki are counting at the same speed.

Danny is counting up in quarters from 2.

Aki is counting down in eighths from 4.

Will they say the same number at the same time?

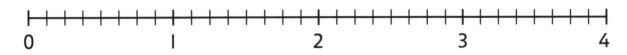

Explain your answer.

_____

_____

Reflect

Mark $1\frac{2}{5}$ on the number line and then complete the sentences.

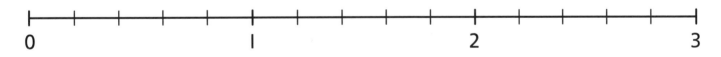

To accurately mark $1\frac{2}{5}$ on the number line I must first

_____

_____

and then

_____

_____

→ Textbook 3B p188

Fractions as numbers ③

1 Identify the fractions shaded. Write the fractions in the boxes.

a)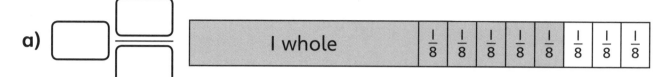

b)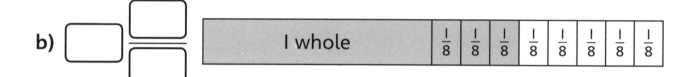

c)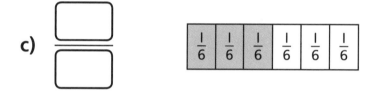

d)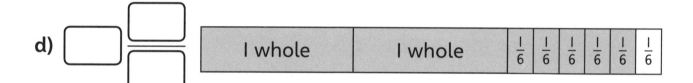

e) Place the 4 fractions that you have identified on the number line.

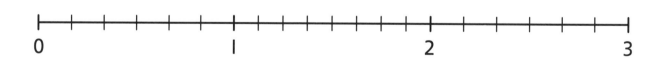

2 What fractions are shown by letters A, B and C on the number line?

Explain your answers.

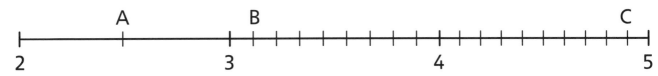

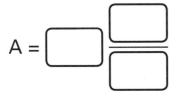

This is because _____

_____

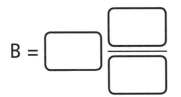

This is because _____

_____

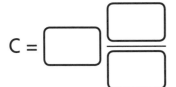

This is because _____

_____

3 Toshi is $1\frac{3}{4}$ metres tall. His nephew, Kit, is $\frac{1}{8}$ metre shorter than 1 metre. Mark both of their heights on the number line.

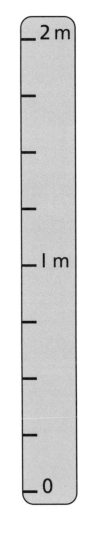

4 Starting with the section of the number line below, complete the number line up to 3 and back to 0.

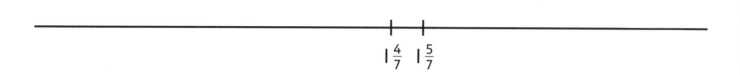

$1\frac{4}{7}$ $1\frac{5}{7}$

5 Mark $2\frac{7}{8}$ on the number line below.

CHALLENGE

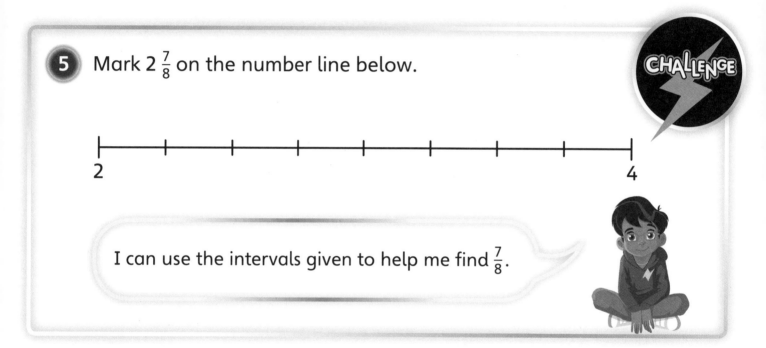

2   4

I can use the intervals given to help me find $\frac{7}{8}$.

Reflect

Explain how you would place $1\frac{5}{8}$ on the number line below.

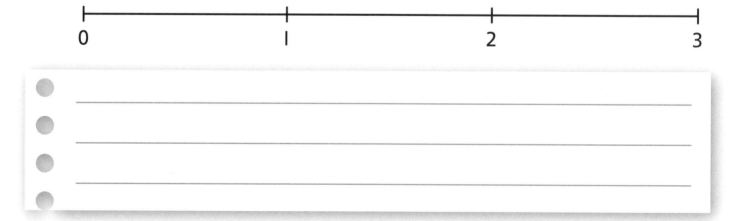

0   1   2   3

Fractions of a set of objects

1 **a)** A school buys 36 new books.

Each class gets $\frac{1}{6}$ of the books.

How many books does each class get?

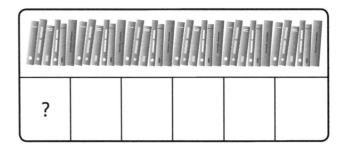

36 ÷ ☐ = ☐

$\frac{1}{6}$ of 36 books = ☐ books

Each class gets ☐ books.

b) The 36 books are shared between more classes.

Now each class gets $\frac{1}{9}$ of the books.

How many books does each class get?

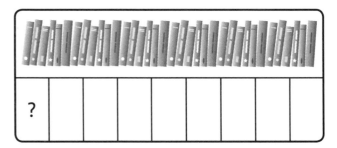

☐ ÷ ☐ = ☐

$\frac{☐}{☐}$ of 36 books = ☐ books

Each class gets ☐ books.

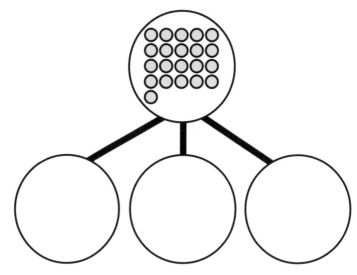

2 $\frac{1}{3}$ of 21 = ☐

3 Amelia cuts a chocolate cake into 5 slices. She wants to decorate the cake with 15 cherries.

How many cherries should she put on each slice so they are all the same?

Amelia should put ☐ cherries on each slice of cake.

4 Zac has 12 sweets in his hand. This is $\frac{1}{2}$ of the whole bag. v

How many sweets are in a whole bag?

?

| 12 | |

$\frac{1}{2}$ of ☐ = 12

There are ☐ sweets in a whole bag.

5 **a)** Luis has a bunch of balloons.

He bursts 8 balloons. This is $\frac{1}{3}$ of the total balloons.

Total number of balloons				
8				

Balloons Luis
bursts

How many balloons did Luis have before he burst any?

Luis had ⬚ balloons to start with.

b) Lee bursts $\frac{1}{4}$ of the remaining balloons.

How many balloons does Lee burst?

Lee bursts ⬚ balloons.

Reflect

Aki has a pack of 30 pencils.

Do you agree or disagree with Aki?

Explain your reasoning to a partner.

I have arranged the pencils into fifths.

$\frac{1}{5}$ of 30 = 5

→ Textbook 3B p196

Fractions of a set of objects ②

 a) Find $\frac{1}{4}$ of 16 flowers.

$16 \div 4 = \boxed{}$

$\frac{1}{4}$ of 16 flowers = $\boxed{}$ flowers

c) Find $\frac{1}{6}$ of 18 glasses.

$\boxed{} \div \boxed{} = \boxed{}$

$\frac{1}{6}$ of 18 glasses = $\boxed{}$ glasses

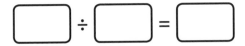

b) Find $\frac{3}{4}$ of 16 flowers.

$16 \div 4 = \boxed{}$

$\boxed{} \times 3 = \boxed{}$

$\frac{3}{4}$ of 16 flowers = $\boxed{}$ flowers

d) Find $\frac{5}{6}$ of 18 glasses.

$\boxed{} \div \boxed{} = \boxed{}$

$\boxed{} \times \boxed{} = \boxed{}$

$\frac{5}{6}$ of 18 glasses = $\boxed{}$ glasses

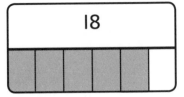

2 $\frac{1}{3}$ of 18

$18 \div 3 = \boxed{}$

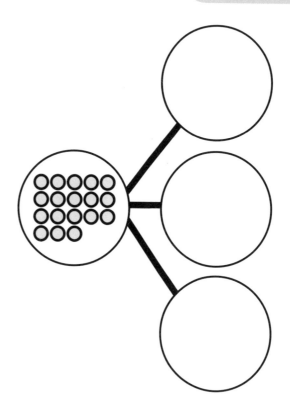

$\frac{2}{3}$ of 18

$18 \div 3 = \boxed{}$

$\boxed{} \times 2 = \boxed{}$

3 A slice of cake has 4 candles on it. This is $\frac{1}{8}$ of the total number of candles on the cake.

How many candles are on the whole cake?

The cake has $\boxed{}$ candles altogether.

4 Join each fraction to its correct answer.

$\frac{2}{3}$ of 12 $\frac{3}{4}$ of 20 $\frac{2}{5}$ of 25 $\frac{7}{8}$ of 16

10   8   15   14

5 Lee has used counters to show $\frac{3}{4}$ of 24. Do you agree with his answer?

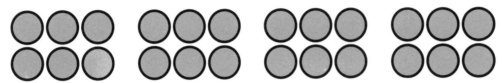

$\frac{3}{4}$ of 24 = 6

I agree / disagree because _____

_____

_____

_____

6 Which would you rather have? Show your working.

$\frac{3}{4}$ of £16   or $\frac{3}{5}$ of £20

_____

_____

_____

Reflect

I can find a fraction of an amount by _____

_____

_____

Fractions of a set of objects ❸

1 **a)** Find $\frac{3}{4}$ of 100 pencils.

$100 \div 4 = \boxed{}$

$\boxed{} \times 3 = \boxed{}$

$\frac{3}{4}$ of 100 pencils = $\boxed{}$ pencils

100 pencils			

b) Find $\frac{2}{3}$ of 180 g of flour.

$\boxed{} \div \boxed{} = \boxed{}$

$\boxed{} \times \boxed{} = \boxed{}$

$\frac{2}{3}$ of 180g of flour = $\boxed{}$ g

180 g

180 g		

c) Find $\frac{2}{5}$ of 95 dog biscuits.

$\boxed{} \div \boxed{} = \boxed{}$

$\boxed{} \times \boxed{} = \boxed{}$

$\frac{2}{5}$ of 95 dog biscuits = $\boxed{}$

95 dog biscuits				

d) Find $\frac{3}{8}$ of 32 km.

$\boxed{} \div \boxed{} = \boxed{}$

$\boxed{} \times \boxed{} = \boxed{}$

$\frac{3}{8}$ of 32 km = $\boxed{}$ km

32 km							

2 A piece of ribbon was 32 cm long.

$\frac{3}{4}$ of the ribbon was used to wrap a present.

What length of ribbon was used?

32 cm			

[ ] cm of ribbon was used.

3 Finley's garden is 60 m long.

$\frac{5}{6}$ of the garden is being planted with flowers.

How many metres of the garden will have flowers? Show your working.

[ ] m of the garden will have flowers.

4 Use the fact $\frac{1}{5}$ of 60 = 12 to find the missing numbers below.

a) $\frac{2}{5}$ of 60 = [ ]

b) $\frac{[\ ]}{[\ ]}$ of 60 = 48

c) $\frac{3}{5}$ of [ ] = 36

5 Complete the calculations.

a) $\dfrac{\boxed{}}{\boxed{}}$ of 48 = 32

b) $\frac{2}{3}$ of $\boxed{}$ = 18

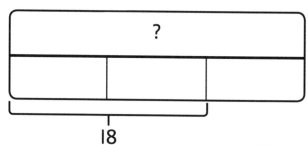

6 $\frac{3}{4}$ of a race will always be a longer distance to run than $\frac{1}{2}$ of a race.

Is this always, sometimes or never true? Explain your answer.

CHALLENGE

_____

_____

_____

_____

_____

Reflect

Explain how you would work out $\frac{3}{5}$ of 80.

First _____

then _____

_____

→ Textbook 3B p204

Problem solving – fractions

1 There are 24 kg of rice in a sack. A restaurant uses $\frac{2}{3}$ of the rice.

How many kilograms of rice are left in the sack?

There are ☐ kg of rice left in the sack.

2

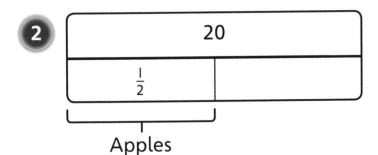

Apples

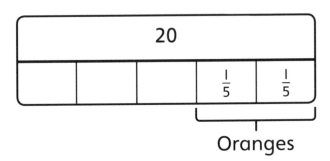

Oranges

There are 20 pieces of fruit in a bowl.

$\frac{1}{2}$ are apples, $\frac{2}{5}$ are oranges and the rest are bananas.

a) How many apples are in the fruit bowl?

$\frac{1}{2}$ of 20 = ☐

There are ☐ apples in the fruit bowl.

b) How many oranges are in the fruit bowl?

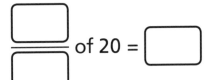 of 20 = ☐

$$☐ \div ☐ = ☐ \qquad ☐ \times ☐ = ☐ \text{ oranges}$$

c) How many bananas are in the fruit bowl?

What fraction is this of the whole?

◻ apples + ◻ oranges = ◻

20 – ◻ = ◻

There are ◻ bananas. This is $\frac{\Box}{\Box}$ of the whole.

3

After the first roll of a dice the counter is moved $\frac{1}{4}$ of the way along the number track.

After the second roll of the dice it is moved another $\frac{1}{5}$ of the way along the track.

What number does the counter finish on?

$\frac{1}{4}$ of 20 = ◻ $\frac{1}{5}$ of 20 = ◻   ◻ + ◻ = ◻

The counter finishes on number ◻ .

4 $\frac{2}{3}$ of a group of children are boys. 18 children in the group are girls.

How many children are there in the group?

There are ◻ children in the group.

⑤ Holly has baked some blueberry, chocolate chip and raspberry muffins.

$\frac{1}{8}$ of the muffins are blueberry.

$\frac{3}{8}$ of the muffins are chocolate chip.

There are 12 raspberry muffins.

How many muffins did Holly bake in total?

CHALLENGE

You could use a bar model to help.

Holly baked ☐ muffins.

Reflect

$\frac{1}{12}$ of 60 = 5

What other fraction number sentences can be written from this fact?

End of unit check

My journal

I   Here is a representation that has been used to solve a problem.

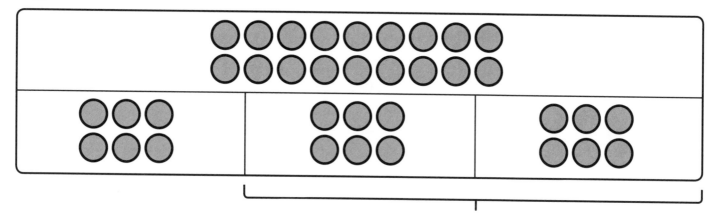

What question could have been asked?

_____

_____

_____

_____

What calculation would fit this question?

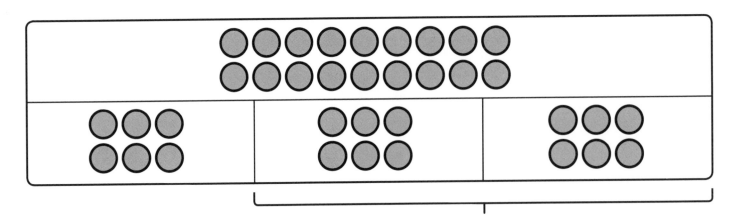

2 Can you think of more than one possible question?

_____

_____

_____

_____

_____

_____

Power check

How do you feel about your work in this unit?

Power puzzle

I wonder if it is possible to share some of the food and drink out in different ways. I would give them one carton of juice each.

Toshi and Jen are going on a picnic.

They want to share the following items of food between them.

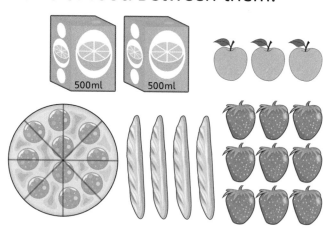

I would give each of them half of each of the juice cartons.

Is it possible to share all these items of food?

_____

_____

_____

How much of each item of food will they each get?

Write number sentences that show how each item of food will be shared.

_____

_____

_____

My power points

Colour the ☆ next to the topics you have done.

Colour the ☺ when you feel confident about the topic.

Unit 5

I can ...

☆ ☺ Compare multiplication and division statements using the < and > signs

☆ ☺ Use times-table facts to solve problems

☆ ☺ Multiply a 2-digit number by a 1-digit number

☆ ☺ Divide a 2-digit number by a 1-digit number

☆ ☺ Solve problems involving addition, subtraction, multiplication and division

Unit 6

I can ...

☆ ☺ Record money in pounds and pence

☆ ☺ Convert between pounds and pence

☆ ☺ Add and subtract amounts of money

☆ ☺ Make change

Unit 7

I can ...

☆ ☺ Interpret and present data using a pictogram

☆ ☺ Interpret and present data using a bar chart

☆ ☺ Interpret and present data using a table

Unit 8

I can ...

☆ ☺ Measure length in mm and cm

☆ ☺ Convert between mm and cm, cm and m

☆ ☺ Order lengths in mm, cm and m

☆ ☺ Add and subtract lengths

☆ ☺ Measure the perimeter of a 2D object

Unit 9

I can ...

☆ ☺ Explain what a unit fraction is

☆ ☺ Explain what a non-unit fraction is

☆ ☺ Count up and down in tenths

☆ ☺ Add two fractions to make a whole

☆ ☺ Place fractions on a number line

☆ ☺ Find a fraction of a set of objects

Keep up the good work!

Notes